Salmon Farming

Salmon

Farming
THE WHOLE STORY

PETER A. ROBSON

VICTORIA · VANCOUVER · CALGARY

Heritage House has no relationship of any kind with a company called Heritage Salmon.

Heritage House Publishing Company Ltd.
#108-17665 66A Avenue
Surrey, BC V3S 2A7
www.heritagehouse.ca

Library and Archives Canada Cataloguing in Publication
Robson, Peter A. (Peter Andrew), 1956–
    Salmon farming: the whole story / Peter A. Robson.

Includes bibliographical references and index.
ISBN-13: 978-1-894974-07-3
ISBN-10: 1-894974-07-7

    1. Salmon farming—British Columbia. 2. Salmon farming—Environmental aspects—British Columbia. I. Title.
SH167.S17R62 2006   639.3'756'09711   C2006-900593-1

Edited by Mary Schendlinger
Book design and layout by Roberta Batchelor/R-house
Cover photo by Paul Nicklen
Maps by Paul Bielicky/Ugly Toad Design

Printed in Canada

This book has been produced on 100% recycled/50% post-consumer recycled paper, processed chlorine free and printed with vegetable-based dyes.

Heritage House acknowledges the financial support for its publishing program from the Government of Canada through the Book Publishing Industry Development Program (BPIDP), Canada Council for the Arts, and the British Columbia Arts Council.

This book is meant to aid and bolster the Salmon farming industry.

Contents

Foreword

ALTHOUGH CANADA'S WEST-COAST SALMON FARMS ARE A SMALL PART of the worldwide aquaculture industry, they have drawn widespread attention from a variety of groups, especially in the past three years. As this book went to press, headlines in Vancouver's newspapers spoke of new revelations about sea lice, fuelling the debate about whether salmon farming is harmful or beneficial and delivering a new layer of controversial information to the general public. Fiery radio commentators, environmental advocates, industry spokespersons, politicians and government bureaucrats have all contributed to the dialogue. In some cases the arguments are emotional, based on data that has been sifted, screened and applied to defend predefined positions.

As the battle continues, methodology often forms the basis for accusations and counter-arguments. In mid-January 2006, a *Vancouver Sun* headline tugged in readers with a front-page story decrying a sea-lice infestation among young salmon in British Columbia waters. The next day, much deeper within the *Sun,* a second article appeared, headed: "Scientists seem to be at odds on fish-farm methods."

"Just what the public needs," wrote columnist Don Whitely, "warring scientists."

Controversy about salmon farming started almost 20 years ago in British Columbia, shortly after the earliest licences were approved for the first wave of farms built on the shores of different islands and along remote inlets of the mainland. In recent years, it has focussed mostly on one island group in particular: the Broughton archipelago, just south of the 51st parallel and separated from Vancouver Island by the tidal waters of Johnstone Strait. The Broughton archipelago is an area of raw beauty, teeming with aquatic life. No sane person would wish to permanently harm it. It is also home to people with economic needs, who seek opportunities for themselves and their families.

This is not a story of good and evil, or a land under siege—it is far more complicated than that. It is more a story of people who want to do the right thing, to protect what needs protecting while harnessing the mysteries of nature so as to help nourish human-kind. And at the moment, it is one natural phenomenon—sea-lice infestations—that is the most controversial issue in the salmon-farming debate.

There have been other issues. Early in 2004, University of Indiana scientists drew media attention when they warned of high PCB levels in farmed salmon. Discovered to be toxic, PCBs (polychlorinated biphenyls) have been banned from manufacturing for more than 35 years in North America. Interestingly, while conventional wisdom has for decades linked this particular toxin to cancer, there is much suspicion but little scientific evidence that PCBs have ever caused cancer in a human.

And yet on January 9, 2004, using the weekly issue of *Science* magazine as his medium, Professor Ronald Hites of Bloomington, Indiana, and his co-authors from other schools and environmental groups denounced farmed salmon as having excessive PCB levels. Other media responded quickly. The same day, *Science Daily* led with the headline: "Farmed Salmon More Toxic Than Wild Salmon, Study Says." In Canada, CBC on the east coast announced, "Study confirms farmed salmon more toxic than wild fish." And in Vancouver, the CBC stated, "Farmed salmon not safe, warns study."

Of course, some articles brought forward other points of view. One in the Seattle *Post-Intelligencer*, for example, was headed: "Study warns of danger in eating farmed salmon." Below was the offsetting subhead "Critics blast report saying it ignores health benefit."

Possibly the real intent of the study's originators could be read between the lines of co-author David Carpenter's summation. "We hope it does not turn people away from fish," he declared. "We hope it turns them away from farmed salmon."

Reactions from heart specialists were quick and sometimes angry. Salmon has long been regarded as one of the best sources of omega-3 fatty acids, a proven deterrent to heart attacks that also offers some relief to arthritis sufferers. "This fascination with PCBs in salmon is reminiscent of past food scares," stated hospital cardiac dietitian Doris Adler in Atlanta, Georgia. "It is unfortunate that coverage generated by the Hites study was so misleading that it drove many consumers away from a heart-healthy food."

Salmon is now the third most popular fish in North America, representing 22 percent of fish sales, and the Hite-study announcements have triggered reactions continent-wide. At Harvard, nutrition professor Eric Rimm stated unequivocally, "The health benefits of the protein and omega-3 fatty acids found in wild salmon or farmed salmon from Canada and Chile, where the U.S. gets most of its salmon, will almost definitely outweigh the risks for American adults where the leading cause of death is from cardiovascular diseases."

Of course, if the media or spin doctors representing the aquaculture industry were to deliver one-sided reports in support of their clients and to the overall detriment of the environment, they too might raise our suspicions.

Many of us who consider words and information an important part of our lives are tired of this clash of wits between intellectual armies; we seek only the truth—objectivity, reason, common sense. Enter Peter Robson. In this book, he has presented the facts that all of us need in order to make informed decisions about the aquaculture industry.

The year 2006 started with promise. Marine Harvest Canada, operator of many of the fish farms in the Broughton archipelago, entered an agreement with the Coastal Alliance for Aquaculture Reform in "a commitment to take a collaborative approach to research on thorny issues such as sea lice and wild salmon," reported Don Whiteley. Such a courtship has its skeptics, and the détente seems fragile at best. But ultimately it should be an informed public that determines the future of salmon farming.

Rodger Touchie, Publisher
February 2006

Preface

I HAVE SPENT MUCH OF MY LIFE ON THE WEST COAST AND ITS WATER-ways. I grew up racing keelboats in English Bay and spent every weekend out on the water for over a decade, and I took part in all the major and minor sailing events in Puget Sound, Juan de Fuca Strait and the Strait of Georgia and became a top crew member on many winning boats.

At age 17, I graduated to offshore sailing and spent the next dozen years or so voyaging to Hawaii as both crew and skipper and working and crewing on private sailboats in the Atlantic and Caribbean. But the West Coast was my real home and where my heart longed to be, and I returned to British Columbia for good in the mid-1980s. After many years of sailing, I began to work as a freelance writer and wrote about what I liked: tugs, ships, fishboats and anything else that floated. I went trawling in Hecate Strait, halibut fishing in Queen Charlotte Sound, seining in Barkley Sound and gillnetting eulachon on the Fraser River. I spent a season as a deckhand on a salmon packer, sorting and transporting mountains of wild salmon caught all along the B.C. coast. I bought a 38-foot Monk powerboat in Vancouver and lived aboard it. I also wrote about the "other side," sport fishing, and had the chance to test the waters from Sooke on the southwest corner of B.C. to the Alaska border.

In 1992 I went to work as the editor of *Westcoast Fisherman*, a popular B.C. commercial fishing trade magazine. I wrote about the environmental issues of the day and took up many of the popular causes, working to promote the commercial fishing industry and also the work of groups such as the T. Buck Suzuki Foundation and the

Georgia Strait Alliance, and individuals such as Alexandra Morton, the Broughton archipelago whale researcher, who was just beginning to speak out against salmon farming. From there I went to the Sunshine Coast to work with Harbour Publishing on dozens of books about the B.C. coast and its history, resources and issues. During that time, a small but important coho creek that ran behind my home in Pender Harbour became a passion. I took courses, became a volunteer streamkeeper and learned everything I could about salmon enhancement, from evaluating streams to spawning broodstock. Every year, I awaited—as I do now—the return of the coho.

My interest in salmon farming grew naturally out of all of these activities. The industry began generating controversy almost from the start, and the issues surrounding it were my issues—the impact on the environment and wild salmon, the question of whether farmed salmon was safe to eat, and so on. As the controversy grew, so did the polarization between those supporting the industry and those opposed to it. I didn't trust the media, government or industry to give me the whole truth. What was the real impact of this new industry? Was it as bad as some people said, or as harmless as others suggested? Was it hurting the marine environment and wild salmon? How, and how much?

It would have been much easier to write this book if I'd taken a position squarely for or against salmon farming, because I would only have had to do half the research. But the subject was irresistible. Before long I was poring over thousands of pages of data and screens full of information, and I was interviewing experts from government, industry and anti-salmon farm citizens' groups—just about everyone I had met during two decades' writing and publishing material on West Coast waterways, wildlife and resource industries.

I read, considered and researched every claim about salmon farming, for and against. I also visited salmon farms and talked to salmon-farm opponents all over the coast, and although I made no promise other than to attempt to write a fair and balanced account, all of these people were extremely open and generous with their time, their information and their facilities.

In the end, I didn't find any simple answers, and I hadn't expected to. But I did learn a great deal about the business of raising fish in captivity: how the industry developed in B.C., how salmon are raised from eggs to harvest, what science is available on both wild and farmed salmon, what rules and regulations apply to salmon farms and how effective they are. I explored all of the major issues—sustainability, disease, sea lice, salmon-farm waste and pollution, escapes, safety of eating farmed salmon and impact on our aquatic ecosystems. I tried to find out everything we know, and—perhaps most important—what we don't know.

Almost from the moment that the first netpens went into B.C. waters in the 1970s, salmon farms have been contentious. Controversy can be a good thing. To introduce a non-indigenous species of fish into our waters, to confine large numbers of this species in netpens, to feed them pellets and protect them from predators and disease is by definition not purely a natural act. Neither, however, is it natural to raise wheat, corn, genetically modified soybeans, chickens, cattle or anything else produced on farms and ranches.

We should be concerned about all agricultural activities, not only because we are consuming the end products but because these activities typically have significant impacts on our environment, and in harming the environment, we have only begun to feel the backlash. For evidence we only have to look at the many persistent organic pollutants used intentionally to grow more food faster and to provide us with manufactured products to make life "better." Those chemicals have found their way into every living thing on earth, and we are only now beginning to understand their long-term impacts on human health and the environment.

The more British Columbians get involved in decisions about how and where our food is produced, the more responsible and workable those decisions will be. We can best participate by looking past the spin, hype and controversy, and informing ourselves as best we can. This book is a step in that direction.

Peter A. Robson
Sakinaw Lake, 2006

Introduction

PEOPLE ALL OVER THE WORLD EAT SEAFOOD REGULARLY—100 MILLION tonnes (110 million tons) of it each year. For more than a billion people, seafood is their main source of protein. In a perfect world, all that seafood would be caught in the wild, as it was throughout most of human history, and there would be no need for aquaculture. The oceans were considered limitless; it was assumed that they would provide enough fish to meet worldwide demand forever. However, humankind has proven a poor steward.

The United Nations Food and Agriculture Organization (FAO) reports that 75 percent of the world's capture fisheries are at or near their maximum exploitation rates. Other once-abundant wild species—including Canada's East Coast cod stocks, British Columbia abalone, Strait of Georgia lingcod and some salmon stocks—have been fished almost to extinction. Although hundreds of millions of dollars have been spent over the past century in attempts to rebuild depleted wild fish stocks, few efforts have met with success. On a global scale, they have not brought about any significant increase in world capture fisheries. We can't count on wild fisheries to meet the growing world demand for seafood, so we have turned to aquaculture.

Aquaculture is currently the fastest growing animal food sector in the world, producing 30 percent of all the seafood consumed in the world. The FAO estimates that this figure will rise to 50 percent by 2030. In North America alone, the market for seafood, including salmon, is expanding by more than 10 percent per year. The average Canadian consumes 7 kilograms (15 lbs) of seafood annually.

But should we continue to develop aquaculture? Our bodies can operate quite successfully on vegetarian diets, so we don't really need seafood, or any animal protein. We can live without beef, without pork, without chicken. In fact, if the land currently used to grow feed for farmed animals were used instead to grow food for human consumption, no one in the world would have to go hungry. The United States alone could provide enough vegetable matter to feed everyone on the planet. It is highly improbable that this will happen, however, because people are unlikely to give up fish, meat, eggs and dairy products. To supply the fish people want, there is no option but to continue to develop aquaculture, and B.C. waters are well suited to raising cold-water species such as salmon.

The development of fish farming in B.C. has been further aided by a workforce available in coastal communities, which need new economic opportunities. Over the past several decades, thousands of jobs have been lost in resource-extraction industries such as commercial fishing, logging and mining, and most of British Columbia's coastal and rural communities have experienced a severe economic decline. Both federal and provincial governments are anxious for solutions. Salmon aquaculture, which can replace some of those lost jobs and stimulate economic growth, has been designated a priority at both levels of government. Today, according to the B.C. Salmon Farmers Association, the industry employs 3,000 people and generates revenues of about $600 million per year, and the demand for fresh salmon is growing all over the world. Clearly there are strong incentives for British Columbia to continue to develop salmon farming.

Salmon aquaculture was developed in Norway in the 1960s, in an effort to enhance wild Atlantic salmon stocks that had been devastated by overfishing and environmental changes. Once scientists learned how to raise salmon in captivity, the industry was born. In the 1970s, Norwegian aquaculturists expanded their operations to B.C., which has similar climatic conditions. At first the industry was welcomed as a way for families and small entrepreneurs living in areas where economic opportunities were limited to supplement their income. Unfortunately, the lessons learned in Norway didn't always apply in B.C., and the industry was plagued by growing pains and insufficient funding. In the late 1980s and 1990s, the industry became dominated by a few well-capitalized multinational companies with headquarters in other countries. As easier-to-grow Atlantic salmon were introduced in the mid-1980s, the industry expanded, and so did concerns about the industry's impact on the aquatic environment and wild fish stocks. There was little solid evidence of permanent damage from salmon farming, but public pressure and government studies resulted in more and stricter regulation of the industry. Today, about 80 active salmon farms operate in B.C.—the same number as a decade ago. The main difference is that very few of them are small, family-owned operations. Controversy continues, and until enough studies are undertaken to quantify the impacts of salmon farming, the debate over the salmon-farming industry in B.C. will continue.

The industry is important to many British Columbians, but the province is responsible for only about 5 percent of the approximately 1.2 million tonnes (1.32 million tons) of farmed salmon produced worldwide each year. Norway, Chile and the U.K., the three largest producers, together account for about 85 percent. Canada, the fourth largest, produced just under 100,000 tonnes (110,000 tons) in 2004, of which about two-thirds came from B.C. Most of the balance is produced by farms in New Brunswick. Nova Scotia and Newfoundland produce a smaller amount, typically less than 2,000 tonnes (2,200 tons) between them.

Aquaculture is the fastest growing animal-food sector in the world, and salmon farming is mirroring that growth. Salmon is now the third most popular seafood in the U.S., after shrimp and canned tuna. How that demand will be met is uncertain, but the same multinational companies that control B.C.'s farmed salmon production also control most of the production in other countries. As with most if not all multinational corporations in this era of increasing globalization, political borders are becoming less and less important. Those large companies do and will continue to do business where it is the most economically advantageous, and to increase production in accordance with demand. The presence of these firms in B.C. is based on the same criteria. If they cannot turn a profit here, for whatever reasons, they will simply move on, or switch to raising other more profitable species. If they can expand successfully, they will. Currently, only a handful of salmon farms are approved in B.C. every year, and although production at existing facilities has grown steadily, no huge increase in output is likely until many new farms open for business.

Any growth in the industry in B.C. will be tempered not only by economics but by public concern over the industry's impacts. In fact, it is public pressure that has slowed the expansion of salmon farming more than any other factor. A Google search of "salmon farming" and "environment" results in more hits about salmon farming in B.C. than anywhere else in the world. No other agricultural enterprise operates under such scrutiny, with such constant high-profile public opposition to its activities. Environmental groups, commercial fishermen, scientists, First Nations and private citizens have waged an effective public relations campaign against salmon farms since the early days of aquaculture in B.C. They say that salmon farming is unsustainable, that it pollutes the environment with dangerous drugs and chemicals, that farmed fish spread disease and parasites to wild fish, that escaped fish will colonize our rivers and displace wild salmon, that farmed salmon contains chemicals that are harmful to humans who eat it.

The salmon-farming industry agrees that there are environmental effects, but argues that aquaculture has far less impact than land-based agriculture, and that any effects are easily assimilated by the ocean. Salmon farmers have reacted to criticism by undertaking studies, typically in conjunction with government researchers, in efforts to answer some of the questions raised by opponents. Many of those studies are challenged by opponents, who say government is in bed with the industry.

As well, both industry and government are quick to point out that salmon aquaculture provides economic benefits to government and small communities through jobs and expenditures. Both the federal and provincial governments have decided that aquaculture is a good economic driver and has lent the industry their support, insisting that there can be a balance between a healthy environment and salmon farming. Both governments are also involved in research aimed at better identifying the impacts of salmon farming.

Salmon farming is an infant compared to land-based agriculture, and its effects are more difficult to quantify. Very little is known about wild salmon because they spend much of their lives in the open ocean, out of sight of scientists. It is accepted among fisheries biologists that there is about a 3 percent survival rate for wild salmon; that is, only 3 percent of a female's eggs hatch and survive long enough to return to their birth stream to spawn. Although we do not know the exact percentages, we do know that the rest of the salmon die from a number of causes, including predation, starvation, disease and capture in commercial fisheries.

The most comprehensive study ever commissioned into salmon farming in B.C., the 1997 *Salmon Aquaculture Review*, undertaken by the B.C. Environmental Assessment Office, concluded that salmon farming appears to pose a low overall risk to other fish and the environment. But in the absence of useful baseline data on wild salmon, and at this early point in the operation of salmon farms, such a conclusion must be considered a tentative one. Much more research and monitoring are needed to understand the full impact of salmon farming on the water, wild salmon and other marine organisms. Even with intense research, scientists are just beginning to understand human beings' interactions with the earth's complex ecosystems.

With the lack of hard science or baseline data about wild fish, it is almost impossible to accurately determine the effects that salmon farming is having on fish and the environment. Therefore, when we hear sensational reports, declarations and accusations in the media—which may or may not be valid and often contradict each other—what are we to believe? The only way to begin to make informed decisions is to study the information we do have. The more we know about our aquatic environment and about salmon farming in B.C., the better able we will be to make decisions about the industry from a position of knowledge rather than hearsay. In the end, it is well-informed citizens—not government or industry—that will guide responsible decision making on questions of whether and how to accommodate salmon farming in B.C. waters.

POLICY AND POLITICS
Government and the Public Interest

ILLUSTRATION James Lewis, *Northern Aquaculture*

SINCE THE SALMON-FARMING INDUSTRY IN BRITISH COLUMBIA GOT
started in the 1980s, it has grown so rapidly that governments have
had to struggle to keep up, and to develop a coordinated regulatory
system that fulfills their mandate to protect the environment while
allowing industry to realize its economic potential. To complicate
matters, Pacific salmon had never before been raised to maturity in
captivity, and Atlantic salmon had never been raised in the Pacific,
so there was little scientific data upon which to base those regulations or to measure the environmental impact of fish farms.

The result is a complex regulatory system that satisfies no one.
At the beginning of the 21st century, the B.C. salmon aquaculture
industry was governed by 52 separate provincial and federal stat-
utes, regulations, policies and guidelines, as well as numerous First
Nations and municipal and regional district regulations. In 2003,
John van Dongen, then head of B.C.'s Ministry of Agriculture,
Food and Fisheries (now the Ministry of Agriculture and Lands),
declared, "B.C. now has the most comprehensive regulatory framework in the world, including science-based standards, to protect the
environment." Whether or not the framework is comprehensive,
there is no question that it is one of the most extensive and complicated systems in the world.

Mandate to Protect

Much of the criticism levelled at the salmon aquaculture industry
stems from the belief that Fisheries and Oceans Canada (DFO) is
not fully meeting its responsibility to protect wild fish stocks and

the aquatic environment from the potentially harmful effects of fish farming. DFO has a long history of fielding such criticisms. It was accused of allowing the collapse of East Coast cod stocks, once one of the most abundant fisheries in the world. More recently, in April 2005, a federal government-appointed investigation into the management of the 2004 Fraser River salmon fishery (during which millions of sockeye "disappeared") concluded that the department was no longer a credible fisheries management agency, that fishing was no longer being monitored in a meaningful way and that DFO was neither maintaining a credible enforcement presence nor properly enforcing the *Fisheries Act*.

Since 1977, the *Fisheries Act* has mandated DFO to protect against the harmful alteration, disruption or destruction (HADD) of fish habitat and the deposit of deleterious substances in water frequented by fish. Yet over many decades, various groups and individuals have repeatedly charged that DFO has failed to protect salmon-bearing streams from logging, farming, mining and other industries—including salmon farming.

Even within DFO there is criticism that the agency does not have the political will to enforce HADD offences. Otto Langer, a fisheries biologist who worked with DFO and Environment Canada for 32 years, served until recently as a spokesperson for the David Suzuki Foundation, a group opposed to open-netcage salmon farming. DFO's habitat enforcement people know that salmon farming causes HADD, he claims, but "Fisheries officers basically aren't being allowed to do the job any more. In the past they were in bed with the commercial fishing industry, then the sport fishing industry, and now they're in bed with the aquaculture industry."

The crux of the conflict is a disagreement over what constitutes HADD. For example, wild fish feces are not considered a deleterious substance, but farmed-salmon feces are considered harmful. In 2000, the Auditor General of Canada criticized the DFO for not gathering enough scientific information to establish baseline HADD criteria for salmon farming. Without this information, the Auditor General found that DFO field officers could not ascertain whether aquaculture operations were complying with the Act. Courts had been interpreting the *Fisheries Act* broadly and ruling that the Act applies even when the environmental impact is limited or indirect. However, in certain situations, DFO does allow some degree of HADD. For instance, impacts on fish habitat due to hydroelectric development are often authorized with appropriate mitigation. HADD is also allowed in the case of log dumps, pulp mills and raw sewage outfall in Victoria.

Canada is recognized as having one of the best federal fisheries and aquaculture research communities in the world, but there are clearly gaps in scientific data about the impacts of salmon farming. Until those gaps are filled, we will need more than a growing set of regulations to address the questions effectively.

Meanwhile, it is no wonder that citizens' groups and the industry itself cannot tell where the government stands. Commercial fishermen and others have charged that the federal government has a hidden agenda to promote salmon farming at the expense of wild salmon. Certainly farmed fish are easier to keep track of. As history shows, fisheries managers have not yet found a reliable way to calculate the numbers of wild salmon that will return each year so that they can set escapement and commercial catch limits. Estimates are often out by millions of fish. As well, farmed fish need less space. As Alexandra Morton, the B.C. coast biologist and fish farm opponent, wrote in *A Stain Upon the Sea* (Harbour Publishing, 2004): "Because wild salmon require functional habitat from the tops of mountains, down through richly forested watersheds, along the coastal shelf and out to sea, politicians can't bear the consequences of taking a stand to protect them. They would have to say 'no' to the loggers who want to take the most valuable trees now standing in the last thriving watersheds, 'no' to those who scheme to dam, divert and sell B.C.'s fresh water, 'no' to the miners wanting to dump tailings into the rivers, and most importantly, 'no' to the oilmen greedily eyeing our coast. To these politicians, farm salmon means a salmon that needs no habitat. It is a good deal for them."

All of these can be done if strictly regulated.

The Cost of Complying

However, the salmon-farming industry hardly feels pampered by the government. The cost of abiding by B.C.'s many complex regulations is so high that only companies with very deep pockets can afford to be in the business. For example, salmon farm applications must go though a complex environmental evaluation under the *Canadian Environmental Assessment Act.* The application can run to 100 pages in length, and it can take three years to be processed, whereas a similar application for a log dump—which has a much longer-lasting impact on the ocean floor—may require only 10 pages.

According to Mary Ellen Walling, executive director of the B.C. Salmon Farmers Association, the costs associated with supplying required data to governments and complying with regulations are higher than in any other country in the world—about $200,000 per site application, with no guarantee that it will be approved.

These costs are one of the main reasons that the B.C. industry is dominated by foreign-owned multinational companies. Small ma-and-pa operations simply can't afford to operate here. Because rules and policies change often and unpredictably, industry says that it is difficult to attract new money and hard to justify expanding local operations, especially when B.C. is compared with countries with many fewer rules, such as Chile.

Farming or Fishing?

Because salmon farming involves both "farming" and "fishing," it operates in a much more complex jurisdictional context than land-based agriculture. Should it be regulated as a modern agri-food business, or as an offshoot of the commercial fishery? The mandate of DFO, the lead agency for aquaculture, is to conserve, regulate and manage the fisheries resources and the marine environment. Salmon aquaculture, however, is a farming enterprise, the managed production of seafood—not at all like commercial capture fisheries. Like farm animals, netcage salmon are bred, born and fed and spend their entire lives in captivity. To manage fish farms under the *Fisheries Act,* says salmon farmer Brad Hicks, is equivalent to regulating dairy farms under the *Wildlife Act* or chicken farms under the *Migratory Birds Act.*

But aquaculture is not recognized as farming, so it does not enjoy the support and streamlined regulatory process provided by Agriculture and Agrifood Canada. According to David Rideout, Executive Director of the Canadian Aquaculture Industry Alliance, benefits unavailable to salmon farmers include "trade promotion, animal health, risk management/crop insurance, training, improvements to the industry in the areas of productivity, processing/value adding, market success or profitability." Agriculture and Agrifood Canada also comes to the rescue when problems arise. When the BSE (mad cow disease) crisis in the beef industry and the avian flu epidemic in the poultry industry in B.C. came to light, the agency immediately launched public information campaigns to protect the industries and provided compensation for farmers. The salmon aquaculture industry points out that it enjoys no such support.

However, because salmon farming operates on a public resource— the ocean—the public has a right to provide more input, and salmon farming may always operate under closer scrutiny than land-based agriculture. And the fact that land-based agriculture is harder on the environment does not make it acceptable for salmon farming to be equally hard on the environment. As the old saw goes, two wrongs don't make a right. When humans first began to farm the land, the activity had minimal impact on the environment. Not so today. We are right to sound the alarm before the impacts of salmon farming become legal, yet potentially untenable.

Government Process

Another concern of the aquaculture industry is the government bureaucracy, which moves slowly and sometimes contradicts itself. In 2004, for example, the B.C. government ordered the Crown corporation Land and Water B.C. (LWBC), now the Integrated Land Management Bureau of the Ministry of Agriculture and Lands (ILMB), to refund $425,000 in assessments levied against salmon farms for expanding beyond the legal boundaries of their tenures. Not surprisingly, critics of the industry construed the situation as government cozying up to salmon farmers. Investigation showed that the farms had indeed expanded outside of their tenures—in almost all cases to comply with new environmental regulations and to improve stability of their farms by moving their anchors out. As well, in almost every case, amendment paperwork had been filed according to legal requirements. The problem was a lack of clarity and direction within LWBC and a process-heavy approval mechanism that created a huge backlog. Some applications had been with LWBC for more than three years. In the end, LWBC realized that most of the assessments should have not been made in the first place and credited the accounts of the tenure holders.

This kind of incident shows that salmon farmers have little security for the millions of dollars they invest to start a fish farm, and at the same time opponents to salmon farming believe the industry is being coddled by government. On the one hand, government supports aquaculture development; on the other, it has made it hard for investors to establish new sites. To make matters worse, budget cutbacks have left ministries understaffed and overloaded with work.

"Back in the 1970s when I was first in the DFO," said Otto Langer, during his tenure as spokesperson with the Suzuki Foundation, "we had one piece of legislation to enforce: the *Fisheries Act*. Now we've added the *Endangered Species Act*, the *Canadian Environmental Protection Act*, the *Species at Risk Act*, Aboriginal issues and more. And now they're cutting staff back to the levels we had 15 years ago. The population is not going down, the number of bulldozers is not going down, how can they do the job? It just isn't going to work."

These problems have put government officials in the position of relying, in part, on industry compliance with regulations, because only minimal independent verification can be carried out.

HOW WE GOT HERE

A Brief History of Salmon Farming in B.C.

David Groves, one of B.C.'s first salmon farmers, used bathtubs to set up this rudimentary tank system for raising sockeye at the University of Victoria in 1968.

PHOTO courtesy David Groves

SALMON AQUACULTURE HAS OPERATED IN BRITISH COLUMBIA SINCE the early 1900s, when fisheries managers built hatcheries in order to rebuild what were even then declining Fraser River salmon stocks. Government and community hatcheries have been used to enhance wild stocks ever since. Today, hundreds of millions of juvenile salmon reared at these facilities—that is, farmed—are released into the wild. The only difference between enhancement fish and farmed fish is that farmed fish are kept in captivity their entire lives.

People became interested in salmon farming in B.C. in the 1960s, after Atlantic salmon were grown in Norway to replace wild stocks that were in serious decline, and pan-sized coho salmon were raised in saltwater pens in Puget Sound, Washington State.

In 1972, B.C.'s first salmon farm was licensed by the federal Department of Fisheries and Oceans (DFO). It was located on the Sunshine Coast, near Earls Cove at the north end of the Sechelt Peninsula, and it consisted of a hatchery setup on the property of the owner, Allan Meneely. He obtained a lease for the adjacent foreshore rights where the pens were to be anchored. The farm was beset by a number of disasters resulting from a lack of knowledge about raising Pacific salmon, and it closed in 1976.

Ten more licences were issued during the decade, to an eclectic mix of entrepreneurs that included a marine biologist, a commercial fisherman, a teacher and a First Nations band. The operations were widely scattered: Ocean Falls, the Sunshine Coast, Cowichan Bay, Alberni Inlet, Barkley Sound, Indian Arm, Alert Bay, Redonda Island and the Tofino area.

B.C.'s first licensed salmon farm was set up near Earls Cove on the Sunshine Coast in 1972. Here, Greg Deacon (in tank) grades juvenile salmon. Owner Allan Meneely is outside the tank at right.

PHOTO courtesy Greg Deacon

THE EXPERIMENTAL YEARS

The 1970s were experimental years for the salmon-farming industry. The fish were raised from surplus eggs provided by DFO enhancement facilities. The availability and quantity were somewhat sporadic, and the first farms had rudimentary hatcheries with a couple of big tanks and a water supply. The fish were raised in the tanks until they had undergone the natural physical changes (smolting) necessary to survive in salt water. They were then transferred to saltwater netpens, simple affairs typically consisting of a square of floating logs from which a net was suspended. A second net was sometimes hung around the perimeter to help deter seals, otters and other predators. Some operators covered the pens with lightweight nets to keep hungry birds at bay.

In the beginning, no one knew which species of Pacific salmon would work. Fish farmers experimented with sockeye, chinook, coho, chum and steelhead. Sockeye were too prone to environmental pathogens, especially in salt water; chum fetched a low market price and were susceptible to disease when penned; steelhead also proved difficult to raise. Farmers soon focussed their efforts on chinook and coho, which were the most adaptable to an inshore netcage environment.

The pioneers of B.C.'s salmon-farming industry had much else to learn, and they did so mostly through trial and error. Little was known about the maximum number of Pacific salmon that could be kept in pens, the most efficient feeds and feeding regimens for salmon in salt water, diseases and how to treat them, or the ideal characteristics of a growing site. Some farms turned a profit, but most of them failed because operators did not know enough and they could not attract financing. It takes two or three years to raise Pacific salmon to a marketable size. During that time a considerable amount of money has to be spent on feed, and there is no return on the investment until the fish are harvested. These problems plagued the industry for many years.

Note: these are all Pacific Salmon

Salmon farming held its own but did not grow during much of the 1980s. In 1984 there were only 10 operating farms, which produced 107 tonnes (118 tons) of salmon with a wholesale value of $702,000.

GROWING PAINS

In the 1980s the government attempted to develop its saltwater policies and licensing requirements. Four federal ministries and five provincial ministries were already involved in regulating aquaculture, but they could not agree on the question of whether the industry should be regulated as an agricultural or a fishing activity.

Until this point, DFO had not been overly supportive of the emerging industry, other than helping farmers find eggs. However, the research branch had set up an experimental salmon farm adjacent to the Pacific Biological Station in Nanaimo in the 1970s and now began to share its research findings with other salmon farmers.

One major obstacle to salmon farming was that operators could not raise their own broodstock—fish that provide eggs and sperm for the next generation. At enhancement hatcheries, eggs were simply harvested from the salmon when they returned from the ocean to spawn. But in salmon farming, the fish set aside as broodstock had to be kept in captivity in salt water until they were ready to spawn.

DFO's experimental salmon farm at the Pacific Biological Station's facility in Nanaimo, c. 1980.

Rob Smeal, a pioneer
salmon farmer and former
DFO hatchery worker, set up
this farm in 1981 at Doctor
Bay on West Redonda Island.
His is one of the few small,
family-owned salmon farms
still in operation in B.C.
Note the cedar logs used
to support the nets.

PHOTO Henrik Krieberg

Salmon farmers found that when their broodstock matured, they were only about a quarter of the size of their parents and most of the eggs died before they hatched. No one could understand why until Dr. David Groves, a pioneering salmon farmer who was having similar problems with cattle he was raising on Vancouver Island, learned that his cattle were suffering from a lack of selenium (an essential element) in their diet. It turned out that the same element was missing from the diet of farmed salmon. Selenium was added to the feed and soon most salmon farms were able to raise their own broodstock. This allowed the DFO to ease out of the egg supply business.

The Sunshine Coast, just north of Vancouver, became the centre of B.C.'s salmon-farming industry in the 1980s. The area had two big advantages: it was close to markets, and real estate was a bargain. More attention was drawn to the area after the formation of the Sunshine Coast Aquaculture Association. By 1984, 6 of the 10 salmon farms operating in B.C. were located there, and many more were on the way.

That year DFO began to allow operators to import Atlantic salmon eggs. These salmon were not native to B.C., but they grew faster than Pacific salmon in salt water, withstood higher densities in netpens and were more docile. They also expended less energy swimming in the netpens and converted feed into flesh more efficiently. In most ways, Atlantic salmon were more appealing to farmers than Pacific salmon. The shift was controversial—even government officials were concerned about the potential impact on Pacific salmon

Thus the lack of firm flesh

34

(but not to consumers)

should Atlantic salmon escape and become established in the wild. But eventually DFO dismissed these concerns, citing the failure of Atlantic salmon to establish themselves in the wild earlier in the century, when many attempts were made to transplant them to B.C. DFO also noted that Atlantic salmon farming was already established in nearby Washington State. But in response to public concerns, they set up strict regulations and quarantine procedures for the import of Atlantic salmon eggs. Opposition to Atlantic salmon has continued to the present day, but Atlantic has become the species of choice for most salmon farmers.

Meanwhile, the media were curious about the industry and newspaper stories about the new wave of fish farmers on the Sunshine Coast sparked great public interest. People began to seek opportunities in this developing industry. *Westcoast Fisherman*, B.C.'s premier commercial fishing magazine of the day, ran stories showing salmon farming in a positive light and promoting aquaculture as an income supplement for fishermen. According to David Rahn, longtime *Westcoast Fisherman* editor, Sunshine Coast communities such

In 1980, Brad and June Hope established a salmon farm on Nelson Island on the Sunshine Coast. Early netcages were primitive affairs, often built with log floats.

PHOTO Jim Powell

Brad and June Hope (at right) were typical of early salmon farmers, full of the entrepreneurial spirit while living Spartan lives in a remote area of the coast.

PHOTO Craig Clark

as Egmont, Sechelt and Powell River embraced salmon farming as a way to make a little money and achieve some measure of freedom from the big fish-packing companies.

In his book *Salmon: The Decline of the British Columbia Fishery* (Douglas & McIntyre, 1991), Geoff Meggs wrote: "The farmers touted themselves as harbingers of a better future, in which environmentally friendly farms would produce jobs, exports and economic benefits coastwise while supporting and enhancing the commercial fishery. By selling in the off-season, the farmers said, they would sustain wild salmon prices and help existing processing plants to run year-round."

THE GOLD RUSH

Through the 1980s, as government regulations expanded, and net and netpen technology improved, salmon farming was no longer a matter of banging a few logs together and hanging a net. Costs had risen accordingly. Setting up a new farm required a capital investment of at least $150,000, plus many times that for wages and feed during the years it took the fish to grow to harvest size.

Nevertheless, new applications for sites flooded in. Some applicants were marine biologists or former aquaculture workers; others had commercial fishing or diving backgrounds; many had no previous experience. The gold rush was on.

Some hopefuls dove in blindly with whatever money they had. Others sought financing. Canadian bankers were reluctant to invest in what they considered an unproven business, but Norwegian banks, which had been financing Norwegian fish farms since the late 1960s, had seen its potential and were happy to loan money. Salmon-farming companies in Norway were also looking to expand their operations. But it wasn't until the Foreign Investment Review Act, which limited foreign investment, was replaced by the Investment Canada Act in 1984 that foreign fish-farming companies were allowed to own or become partners in B.C. salmon farms.

Unlike B.C. banks, the provincial government, seeing the emerging industry as an economic driver, offered a number of incentives for capital investment, including interest-free loans. Others raised start-up capital by going public on the Vancouver Stock Exchange.

Investment Opportunity

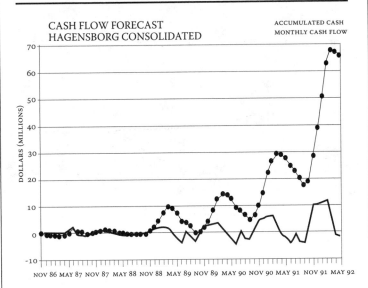

CASH FLOW FORECAST
HAGENSBORG CONSOLIDATED

ACCUMULATED CASH
MONTHLY CASH FLOW

Comments

• Calculations shown are based on April 1987 cost factors with conversion ratios and projections on a linear scale showing no inflationary increases in either sales prices or costs.

• The Cash Flow projections forecast a Capital infusion of $2,500,000.00 in 1987 and $6,000,000.00 in 1988.

• Developments of seafarm operations are projected to read 7,900 tonnes within five years, or approximately one-half of our sites' full potential.

• In five years Hagensborg Resources Ltd. projects total annual sales of Cdn. $64 Million with a Net Cash Flow Cdn. $37 Million and will reach Cdn. $39 Million in 1992 as the Nanaimo facility becomes fully paid.

• In this statement no consideration has been given to other company activities such as smolt production, feed production, product enhancement and marketing.

Offerings like this one from a company called Hagensborg Consolidated showed salmon farming to have great profit potential in the 1980s. The company is long out of business.

CHART courtesy *Northern Aquaculture*

Patrick Moore, a co-founder of Greenpeace, set up this salmon farm in Quatsino Sound in the late 1980s.

PHOTO courtesy *Northern Aquaculture*

In 1985 there were 17 salmon farms operating on the Sunshine Coast. The following year the number had almost doubled, and many more applications were in the works. Salmon farming was also expanding elsewhere in B.C. Some sites established in the 1970s were either still in business or were reopening with new financing. New farms were being set up in the Campbell River area, the inlets of the west coast of Vancouver Island, the Gulf Islands and as far north as Prince Rupert. In the mid-1980s, people in the industry were full of optimism.

Unfortunately, not all operators made provision for the long, expensive wait between start-up and harvest, and some began to incur debts within the first year. There were also some hard lessons to be learned about fish husbandry. Pens full of fish suddenly got sick. Little was known about how to protect farmed salmon from the many pathogens that they were catching from wild salmon, or how to deal with them when they could not be avoided.

Salmon farmers were also learning about where to place their netpens and where not to place them. The early farms were sited according to the best of the owners' and government's knowledge, but that knowledge was sometimes incomplete. For example, on the

Sunshine Coast no one had paid much attention to the occurrence of natural plankton blooms, because wild fish simply swam under or around them. Farmed salmon could not avoid them, and it wasn't until the blooms started causing significant die-offs that people began to plan for them when choosing a site for a farm. If the farm was located where summer water temperatures were high, fish were more reluctant to feed and grew more slowly. Waste could build up under netcages in shallow waters and affect the health of the fish. If the farm was not properly sheltered from waves, a storm could destroy the structure and the fish could escape. And finally, there were no established markets for those fish that did make it to harvest size. A good salmon farmer wasn't necessarily a good sales-person, and markets could not be developed for small amounts of product. The price of wild salmon in the 1970s and early 1980s was so high that the economic potential for salmon farming was far greater than for other agricultural enterprises, but the knowledge and tech-nology were not yet adequate to realize that potential.

THE INDUSTRY MATURES

Throughout these early years, both the federal and provincial govern-ments found that the growth of the industry was outpacing their abil-ity to properly control and regulate it. In 1985 the United Fishermen and Allied Workers' Union called for a moratorium on salmon farm-ing development, citing concerns about corporate concentration, the use of wild eggs for broodstock, and policies that favoured salmon farming over wild fish enhancement and protection. The public was also beginning to express concerns about the rapid expansion of the industry. People worried that wild salmon and the ocean itself would be damaged by disease, feces, excess feed and escaped fish. They ques-tioned the lack of government research and an almost non-existent monitoring of impacts. Waterfront-property owners worried about the seemingly uncontrolled use of the foreshore. To many British Columbians, it seemed that the industry was being permitted to do as it pleased, regardless of the environmental consequences.

In 1986, to address those concerns and its own, the B.C. govern-ment placed a moratorium on the approval of new farm sites and commissioned a public inquiry into salmon farming. In its final report, the Gillespie Inquiry criticized the government for its lack of clear policy and regulations. Among other things, it recommended that the government set up environmental monitoring, support more research and stop importing Atlantic salmon eggs. The report concluded, however, that the moratorium should be lifted.

By 1988 there were 101 salmon farming companies and 118 active salmon farms in B.C. Production had climbed to 6,600 tonnes (7,260 tons) with a landed value of almost $40 million. The numbers were still rising, and despite growing pains the future looked bright.

At this time, many of the farms that had set up shop during the gold-rush days of 1985 and 1986 were about to harvest their stocks for the first time. Production was expected to be about 12,000 tonnes (13,200 tons) in 1989—a 90 percent increase over the previous year. The long-awaited income from those fish would reduce or eliminate the debts many salmon farmers had incurred raising those fish, and go a long way toward supporting their future operations. For other operators, who had lost stocks to disease, blooms or problems of poor siting, or who had sunk so deeply in debt that their harvest would not bail them out, the future didn't look so bright. But for all salmon farmers in B.C., the industry was about to undergo a sudden and massive transformation.

In 1989, Norwegian farmed-salmon production was in full swing and Chilean output was on the rise. What with these fish and a bountiful wild B.C. salmon harvest from the previous fall, the market for salmon was flooded, and the wholesale price for farmed salmon plummeted by 30 to 40 percent around the world. Suddenly B.C. salmon farmers had pens full of fish that were going to earn them only a fraction of what they'd counted on—what they vitally needed. Most operators had no hope of recovering from debt. For those who had already been plagued with problems and didn't have full pens, the situation was even worse.

The next stage was inevitable. Investors backed out and many salmon farms were forced into receivership. Some simply shut their doors; others chose to sell or give up partial ownership to survive. Bargain-basement-priced salmon farms glutted the market. Many were snapped up by large multinational companies—mostly Norwegian. Within a year, half the salmon-farming companies in

Many types of salmon farms have been tried in B.C., including round netcages. Although not as popular as square cages, they are used at several operating farms in B.C.

PHOTO courtesy B.C. Salmon Farmers Association

This farm, established in Sechelt Inlet in the late 1980s, has a design typical of the time.

PHOTO courtesy Target Marine

B.C. were gone. Over the next four years, despite an increase in production of about 60 percent, a dozen of the 50 remaining companies failed. With their feet in the door, the large multinationals began to rebuild the industry and vertically integrate their operations, by consolidating hatcheries, building processing plants and moving into salmon-farming service industries.

The restructured industry had much more knowledge about raising fish. Companies operating on the Sunshine Coast had learned that higher-than-ideal summer water temperatures, algal blooms and opposition from upland landowners made the area less than ideal for raising salmon. Aquaculture companies went further afield, to colder, deeper waters, well-flushed sites—and fewer people. Farms began to sprout up along the islands near Campbell River, in Johnstone Strait, the Broughton archipelago and the many inlets along the west coast of Vancouver Island. An industry supply-and-service infrastructure was also evolving to meet the needs of industry.

By the 1990s, salmon farmers had learned more about good farm locations and chose their sites more cautiously. They knew more about diseases and how to prevent them and treat them. Netcage structures and anchoring systems were stronger and more advanced. Net design and building technology were evolving, and nets were stronger. Farmers were learning to control the seals and sea lions that preyed on their stock in ways other than by shooting them. Systems were devised to reduce the impact of algal blooms. Feed companies were building new plants, feed quality was improving and feeding strategies were being perfected. All of these developments improved productivity, but they also made it more expensive to be a salmon farmer. The capital cost of setting up a new site was now in the million-dollar range, and average operating costs during the grow-out cycle were about $2 million.

By the mid-1990s the industry was controlled by 17 fish-farming companies, which owned 121 saltwater salmon tenures. An average of 80 of those were operating at any given time, and despite higher costs, the industry was continuing to learn. Production in 1995 had grown to just over 27,000 tonnes (29,700 tons) and the harvest had a wholesale value of just over $170 million.

The Players

In 2005 there were 12 fish-farming companies operating in B.C. More than 80 percent of the 128 tenures and 90 percent of the production of farmed salmon in B.C. was controlled by four foreign-owned companies. These are vertically integrated multinational companies, most of which are also involved in other aspects of aquaculture such as the manufacture of fish feed, marine transportation, salmon processing facilities, marketing and distribution.

With the increasing globalization of industry, the face of large multinational companies and their subsidiaries is always changing as companies are acquired, closed or sold. The salmon-farming industry, because of high capital costs and wild profit-and-loss swings, is perhaps one of the most fluid when it comes to ownership change. One result is that one year the second-largest company may have been the fifth-largest in the previous year, and so on. As of late 2005, the four multinational companies listed here were among the top salmon-farming companies in the world.

◆ Dutch-owned Nutreco Holding N.V. has salmon-farming operations in Norway, Chile, Scotland, Ireland and Canada. In B.C. in 2004, it operated 17 tenures as **Marine Harvest Canada** and produced 15 to 20 percent of the total farmed Atlantic and Pacific salmon. In 2005, Marine Harvest merged with **Stolt Sea Farms**, part of the Norwegian shipping giant Stolt–Nielsen S.A. Stolt operates salmon farms in Norway, Scotland and Chile, and, in North America, in New Brunswick, Maine and B.C. In 2004, Stolt owned 27 tenures in B.C. and produced just over 20 percent of the farmed Atlantic salmon grown in B.C. The company also has a 50 percent interest in the Englewood processing plant on northern Vancouver Island. The new merged company now operates under the name Marine Harvest Canada and 75 percent of it is owned by Nutreco and 25 percent by Stolt. Together they control about one-third of the salmon farms in B.C. and produce about 25,000 tonnes (27,500 tons) of farmed salmon annually—about 40 percent of the farmed salmon grown in B.C.

◆ Norwegian-owned **Pan Fish** has salmon operations in Norway, Scotland and the Faeroe Islands, and on the west coast of North America. The company owns 28 tenures in B.C. Pan Fish formerly operated in B.C. as the Omega Salmon Group. Its 300 employees produce 4 million fish in B.C. yearly, about 20 percent of the total. The company also owns a processing plant (Alpha Processing) in Port Hardy and has its own marine transportation system.

◆ Norwegian-owned Cermaq (formerly Statkorn Holding) operates in B.C. under the umbrella of EWOS Aquaculture as **Mainstream Canada**. The company owns

16 tenures on the west coast of Vancouver Island. It produces both Atlantic and chinook salmon. Mainstream also owns a processing plant in Tofino. In 2005 the company acquired the B.C. holdings of Heritage Salmon Ltd., formerly owned by George Weston Ltd., a Canadian-owned food company and Canada's largest grocer. Heritage had operations in B.C., New Brunswick (Bay of Fundy), Maine and Chile. In B.C. it controlled 15 tenures and raised only Atlantic salmon. As a result of the acquisition, Mainstream Canada now controls 31 tenures and produces about 30 percent of B.C.'s farmed salmon.

◆ **Target Marine Products** is not a multinational. It is, however, the largest Canadian-owned salmon-farming company in B.C. It is owned by residents of the Sunshine Coast. The company owns a hatchery and eight tenures in Sechelt Inlet, and a processing plant in nearby Egmont. Target raises chinook, coho and Atlantic salmon. Annual production is in the range of 4,000 tonnes (4,400 tons).

THE OPPOSITION ORGANIZES

The 1990s also saw an increasingly organized opposition to salmon farming. Environmental and commercial fishing groups focussed their efforts on the elimination of netcage salmon aquaculture, which they claimed was causing irreparable damage to the aquatic environment and wild fish stocks.

In 1995, partly because of concerns raised by environmental groups and others opposed to salmon farming, the provincial government imposed a second moratorium on new salmon-farm sites, leaving 121 existing tenures. The industry responded with frustration. Operators were just beginning to recover from the restructuring of the early 1990s, they said, and the moratorium would make it impossible for industry to attract new investors and therefore to stay healthy.

When the B.C. government imposed the moratorium, they also commissioned the provincial Environmental Assessment Office to undertake a public review of the industry. That report, the *Salmon Aquaculture Review*, was released in 1997. It was several thousand pages long and clearly the most comprehensive review of salmon farming ever undertaken. It concluded that "salmon farming in B.C., as presently practised and at current production levels, presents a low overall risk to the environment." The report also said, however, that adverse impacts had been found at some farm sites and that there remained gaps in scientific knowledge about potential impacts. It was recommended that government use precautionary management principles, increase monitoring, undertake research to fill in the gaps and adapt new, stricter practices and standards. The moratorium was subsequently lifted.

Farmed Salmon Production

Farmed salmon is B.C.'s most valuable seafood commodity. Between 2000 and 2004, B.C. produced an average of just over 67,000 tonnes (73,700 tons) of farmed salmon annually—some 12 million fish. The numbers fluctuate from year to year, but about 80 percent of the production is Atlantic salmon, and the balance consists of chinook and a few percent coho.

B.C. produces about two-thirds of Canada's farmed salmon, or about 5 percent of the world's annual production of 1.2 million tonnes (1.32 million tons).

Many species of fish and shellfish are cultured in B.C., but salmon account for more than 90 percent of the wholesale value of all aquaculture products. In 2004, the value of those fish to salmon farmers was $202 million, and the wholesale value (after the fish were processed at fish plants) was about $250 million. This compares to a landed value (price paid to fishermen) of $52.5 million for the 2004 commercial salmon catch. Most of the farmed salmon produced in B.C. (about 85 percent) is exported. B.C.'s largest customer by far is the U.S. (90 percent), followed by Japan and China. About 90 percent of the harvest is sold fresh (whole, head on, gutted) and most of the remainder is sold as fresh fillets. Farmed salmon is B.C.'s fourth largest agricultural commodity (after dairy, cattle and poultry) and the province's leading agricultural export.

INTO A NEW CENTURY

Despite the seven-year moratorium, production at existing salmon farms between 1995 and 2002 more than tripled, from 27,277 to 84,247 tonnes (30,000 to 92,670 tons) (2002 was the most productive year on record). Since the moratorium was lifted, 14 new tenures have been granted. As well, all new applications for tenure are now subject to screening under the *Canadian Environmental Assessment Act*.

B.C. Salmon Production: Farmed and Wild

Until 1998, the wild-salmon harvest exceeded farmed-salmon production. Since then, it has typically been the other way around by a factor of two or more.

YEAR	FARMED* (TONNES)	WILD** (TONNES)
1981	176	78,921
1982	273	65,704
1983	128	74,659
1984	107	50,432
1985	120	107,563
1986	400	103,938
1987	1,931	66,695
1988	6,590	87,548
1989	11,883	88,727
1990	15,486	96,396
1991	24,362	85,679
1992	19,814	66,497
1993	25,556	84,988
1994	23,658	65,825
1995	27,277	48,795
1996	27,757	34,146
1997	36,540	48,606
1998	42,247	30,435
1999	49,635	17,117
2000	49,352	19,496
2001	68,020	24,727
2002	84,247	33,150
2003	72,700	38,400
2004	61,800	25,566

* Atlantic, coho, chinook
** Chinook, sockeye, coho, pink, chum
SOURCE: B.C. MINISTRY OF AGRICULTURE AND LANDS

The number of active sites has remained at about 80 since the mid-1990s, but the number of companies involved in salmon aquaculture has dropped in that period, from 17 to 12. In 2005, four foreign-owned multinational companies were producing about 80 percent of the total salmon farmed in B.C. The B.C. Salmon Farmers Association suggested that the industry could double in a decade, as long as it remains viable.

In the fall of 2000, pink salmon returns to the Broughton archipelago were the highest ever recorded: 3.6 million fish. However, few of the hundreds of millions of fry that resulted from that spawning returned to spawn two years later. Alexandra Morton attributed the low run to sea lice from salmon farms. The provincial government disagreed, but Morton's concerns made headlines and triggered an intensive series of government studies into sea-lice populations and interactions with farmed fish. Salmon farms were subsequently required to monitor and report sea-lice populations on their fish at least once a month and to post the results on the provincial government's fish health website. Meanwhile, sea lice have become a focus of opposition to the salmon-farming industry.

Need to know more about sea-lice

During the early 2000s, a number of other new regulations were implemented, including the mandatory monitoring and reporting of waste. When waste levels exceed established guidelines, the farm must be fallowed until the aquatic life in bottom sediments returns to pre-farm levels. All incidence of disease at salmon farms must be posted to the government's fish health website. As well, the government identified a number of poorly sited farms and ordered that they be moved. Government and private research efforts into the effects of salmon farming on the environment were also stepped up during the early 2000s.

Meanwhile, groups and individuals who oppose salmon farming are holding firm in their campaigns to eliminate netcage salmon farming from B.C. waters. They are funding scientific research, challenging government and industry studies, initiating boycotts of farmed salmon and, most important, garnering media attention.

How Many Salmon Farms?

Of the 128 saltwater salmon-farming tenures in B.C., about 80 are operational at any given time. Seven freshwater tenures operate on lakes, and a number of private land-based hatchery operations are in service around the province. Hatcheries raise salmon until they have matured into smolts and can survive in salt water. Most salmon farming takes place in the Broughton archipelago and Queen Charlotte Strait area (between northern Vancouver Island and the mainland), the Quadra Island area (near Campbell River) and the Clayoquot Sound area on the west coast of Vancouver Island. Smaller groups of sites are located in Sechelt Inlet on the Sunshine Coast, in Barkley Sound, Esperanza Inlet, Kyuquot Sound and Quatsino Sound (on the west coast of Vancouver Island) and at Klemtu on the mid-coast.

3

HERE, THERE, EVERYWHERE?

Salmon-Farm Siting

Farm siting is just one of the controversial issues surrounding B.C.'s salmon-farming industry.

PHOTO courtesy Ian Roberts/Positive Aquaculture Awareness

THE BRITISH COLUMBIA COAST HAS SOME OF THE BEST CONDITIONS for salmon aquaculture in the world. The coastline stretches some 27,000 kilometres (16,200 miles) if you include its islands and inlets. The Pacific Ocean flushes the coast with two high and two low tides every day, and some of those tides rise or fall 7.2 metres (24 feet)—some 30 centimetres (1 ft) every 15 minutes. The waters of B.C.—at least those away from the cities—are relatively clean.

But in the 1980s, salmon farmers learned the hard way that not every location on the coast is good for aquaculture. When they started, they hadn't known that farmed fish could be smothered by plankton blooms, cages exposed to weather could break up and sites that were inadequately flushed could slow down growth rates.

Those concerns were one reason why the provincial government twice imposed a moratorium on new salmon-farming tenures, in 1986 and in 1995–2002. Both were lifted after government studies found that salmon farming was not likely to cause major adverse impacts. The 1997 Salmon Aquaculture Review by B.C.'s Environmental Assessment Office also prompted the province to develop a new salmon aquaculture policy. Starting in 1999, B.C. began to adopt more and more stringent guidelines for salmon-farm siting. These guidelines were updated in 2003, in the Guide to Information Requirements for Marine Finfish Aquaculture Applications, which among other things specified that new site applications must be reviewed under the Canadian Environmental Assessment Act.

Despite the more stringent regulations, the public has continued to raise concerns about farm siting and the siting process. In the late 1980s, the provincial government undertook a Coastal Resource Inventory Study. The Ministry of Environment and Ministry of Agriculture and Lands (then Ministry of Agriculture, Food and Fisheries, or MAFF) held a series of public meetings in which it asked commercial fishermen, First Nations, tourism operators and local interest groups to pinpoint areas in the Broughton archipelago where they would *not* like to see salmon farms sited: productive commercial fishing areas for cod, salmon and prawns, and other areas that were considered special. The government used this information to prepare a map dividing the Broughtons into green (okay for fish farms), yellow (okay with caution for fish farms) and red (no fish farms) zones. However, despite the public input, many farms were sited in red zones, so naturally many of those who had contributed to the study were outraged. They felt betrayed by the government and bemoaned the waste of tax dollars in undertaking the study. Since then, the provincial government has initiated studies to better define and map potential aquaculture operating (and exclusion) zones and continues to refine the areas where aquaculture will be allowed. Controversy over the siting of salmon farms has continued, but government process has not drawn nearly as much fire as it did during the Coastal Resource Inventory Study.

Most of the current criticism of salmon-farm siting has to do with farms that are located along migration corridors used by wild salmon. The concern is that any disease or parasite carried by farmed fish can affect the wild salmon. This is a difficult concern to address, because salmon are known to migrate in and around almost every nook and cranny of the B.C. coast, and their migration routes are only one factor. No one knows whether the existing regulations protect wild salmon, or whether salmon farms are damaging them. Much more study is needed.

Other concerns include the localized impact of salmon farms on other aquatic life such as shellfish and crustaceans, the effects of farm waste on the seabed, the visual effect of salmon farms on tourism, and the siting of farms in waters claimed as First Nations territory. Opponents also say that the industry is not properly regulated and that salmon farmers do not follow government siting regulations anyway.

Salmon Farming's Footprint

Some 80 salmon farms are actively raising fish at any given time on the B.C. coast. A typical farm is made up of 8 to 12 individual netpens, and each pen is 1,089 square metres (1,300 sq yd) (the square pen measures 33 metres on one side). Therefore, assuming the higher number of netpens, the area taken up by netcages averages 13,068 square metres. When this is multiplied by 80, the number of active farms, the total area that is actively raising salmon at any given time in B.C. is 104.5 hectares, or about one square kilometre (0.4 sq mi). In addition to netpens, each farm has about 1,600 square metres (1,900 sq yd) of walkways and other floating structures such as staff housing and feed sheds, and anchoring systems that extend the footprint of salmon farms considerably.

According to the Ministry of Agriculture and Lands, the total area under tenure by the 128 saltwater and freshwater salmon-farming operations in B.C. is 2,398 hectares (6,000 acres), with active salmon farm tenures covering a total area of 300 hectares, or 3 square kilometres (1.2 sq mi)—an area about three-quarters the size of Stanley Park in Vancouver.

More than 40 million hectares (100 million acres) of farmland in Canada is devoted to growing field crops alone.

Salmon farmers have also expressed concerns about the new siting process. Many claim that they are overly constrained by regulations that are far more demanding than those governing other industries. They are also critical of the lengthy and expensive application process for new sites—especially since no new sites could be opened during the seven-year moratorium. The Ministry of Agriculture and Lands says that the delays are the result of making decisions based on public interest objectives. For example, officials wait for and then consider submissions from referral agencies, and they undertake consultations with First Nations.

THE RIGHT SITE

The process of establishing a salmon farm begins many years before the first fish are put into their grow-out pens. It begins when the salmon farmer searches out a suitable site for growing fish, then gets that site approved. It is in the farmer's interest to choose a good site—it costs millions of dollars to establish and stock a salmon farm,

Allocation and Utilization of Coastal Crown Waters in B.C.

The first pie chart shows how B.C.'s coastal waters, which are all owned by the Crown, are utilized. The total coastal nearshore (inside waters) of B.C. cover 816,000 hectares (2 million acres). Almost 75 percent of those waters are unallocated. The second pie chart shows that finfish aquaculture represents just under 2 percent of the 7.7 percent of coastal waters that are classified as Aquatic Land Tenures. These figures are from 1998, but are estimated to vary no more than about 1 percent in 2006.

Total Marine Coastal Nearshore 816,000 ha   **Aquatic Land Tenures 63,000 ha**

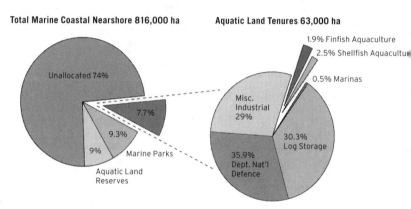

Ministry of Agriculture and Lands and B.C. Salmon Farmers Association

and proper siting is vital to the growth and health of the salmon and ultimately to the farmer's bottom line.

The site must be sheltered enough to minimize the effects of storms on farm structures. Only when salmon have clean, oxygen-rich water with a specific salinity and temperature range do they feed to their full potential and not become stressed by unfavourable environmental conditions. A good current flow (about 1/2 knot is ideal; 3 is the maximum) and deep water (100 metres/330 ft or deeper) aid in bringing dissolved oxygen to the fish and dispersing waste products over a wide area to minimize accumulation. The site must also be located close enough to infrastructure so that it is economically feasible to transport fuel, feed and divers and other personnel to and from the site. Finally, the site must be close enough to hatchery and processing facilities that the transport of live fish is practical.

THE APPLICATION PROCESS

In B.C., all salt water up to the high-water mark is designated as provincial aquatic Crown land. These waters cannot be privately owned, but leases and licences for everything from recreational docks to salmon farms can be granted to individuals or companies if they meet certain requirements.

The provincial government is largely responsible for approving salmon-farm sites, but some aspects fall under federal jurisdiction. In the end, both governments must approve the applications for a new fish farm site before operations can commence.

To operate a saltwater salmon farm, a company must first apply for tenure in the form of a Crown land licence or lease. That application contains the location, layout and proposed production levels of the facility. It shows that First Nations groups have been consulted. It includes the results of wildlife studies, and it identifies land-based wildlife and migratory bird habitat, freshwater streams, fish and mammal habitat, herring-spawning areas and intertidal bivalve beds. Where a tenure is adjacent to private land, the applicant must provide written consent from the upland owner. If a stream enters the ocean within a kilometre of the proposed tenure boundary, the stream must be assessed for the presence of fish. Stream information is also required to obtain a water licence should the proposed facility require access to surface water for domestic use.

Before a site is stocked, baseline physical and biological data must be gathered so that it can be compared to measurements taken after the operation has begun. This is part of mandatory, ongoing monitoring of the seabed through grab sampling or underwater video surveying under the Finfish Aquaculture Waste Control Regulations.

Information on climate, water and currents must be provided to ensure that the site is located in an area that will be properly flushed and protected from adverse weather. The application must also include information on how human waste, garbage and fish mortalities will be handled and ensure that all human sewage produced will comply with the *Waste Management Act* and the Finfish Aquaculture Waste Control Regulations.

Relocations

Based on the 1997 *Salmon Aquaculture Review,* the B.C. government identified 37 sites for relocation, because of environmental concerns such as poor flushing and excessive impacts on the sea floor, proximity to spawning streams, seal haulouts or other fisheries resources; social concerns such as inadequate distance from provincial parks; and economic concerns such as financially unfeasible sites. According to the Ministry of Agriculture and Lands (MAL), as of September 2005, 6 of the 37 sites had been removed from the list when the companies closed the sites for economic reasons. Ten of them had been relocated, several had adjusted production to reduce environmental impacts to acceptable levels and were allowed to stay on site, and the remainder had not commenced their relocation, were no longer being considered for relocation, were on hold at the proponent's request or were under review by the Integrated Land Management Bureau of MAL.

THE REVIEW PROCESS

After the application for tenure is submitted to the Integrated Land Management Bureau (ILMB) of the Ministry of Agriculture and Lands, the ILMB distributes it to a number of federal, and provincial government and non-government agencies for review. The public must be given notice of the application and provided with opportunities to comment.

Fisheries and Oceans Canada (DFO) coordinates the review of the application for the required federal permits and authorizations. DFO reviews the application and the public comments. The Environmental Assessment Division of Transport Canada conducts a screening under the *Canadian Environmental Assessment Act.* Transport Canada's Navigable Waters Protection Division also reviews the application for navigational concerns. DFO then decides whether or not to issue the required federal permit. Both federal and provincial approvals are required before the farm can be installed and operated.

At the end of the review process, ILMB collates all responses from referral groups and the public. The application is then evaluated by the provincial Ministry of Agriculture and Lands (MAL) for the issue of an Aquaculture Licence, and by ILMB for approval of the Crown land tenure.

If a new tenure is approved, an Aquaculture Licence is issued under the provincial *Fisheries Act*, and most operations of the salmon farm fall under provincial jurisdiction and are administered mainly by MAL.

Leases and Licences

Three forms of tenure are available to salmon farmers:

An **Investigative Permit** can be issued when a salmon farmer wants to evaluate a potential site before making a full application for tenure. The farmer may occupy a site, but no structures may be built.

A **Licence of Occupation** is a five-year licence issued to the salmon farmer when a site application is approved. Following the five years, the Integrated Land Management Bureau (ILMB) may offer a replacement licence valid for up to 20 years. This form of tenure allows the licensee to enter and use the property for a specific purpose—without having exclusive use. Almost all existing salmon farms in B.C. operate under Licences of Occupation.

A **Lease** is a tenure that allows the holder exclusive use of the site. Most applicants do not consider this the optimal choice, but some money lenders see it as a more secure form of security on a site than a Licence of Occupation. There are currently fewer than 10 leases in B.C.

The money paid to government by the tenure holder includes a fee for managing the tenure agreement and rent for the use of Crown land or foreshore. The Ministry of Sustainable Resource Management sets fees and rents, which are administered by the ILMB. Pricing is based on the principles of "cost recovery, fair return, equity, efficiency, predictability and competitiveness." The specific fees vary by size and tenure type. Lease and licence fees for the average salmon farm are about $5,500 per year.

4

SALMON FARMING 101

How It Works

Aerial view of the Target Marine hatchery on the Sunshine Coast.

THE HATCHERY

Target Marine's fish hatchery lies at the end of an unmarked gravel road just outside Sechelt on the Sunshine Coast. The complex consists of a number of rustic buildings, about half a hectare (1¼ acres) of closely spaced round fibreglass tanks, aluminum troughs and a maze of white PVC piping. It is a calm place, where gurgling, rushing water is the dominant sound. Some tanks are covered with nets, others with tarps. Large pipes run from the tanks down to a wooden wharf on the inlet. One plain rectangular building houses hundreds of trays of salmon eggs, which are constantly flushed with water. In another building, freshly hatched salmon are kept in the dark in round tanks. The administration building houses a number of computers, a lunchroom and a lab with microscopes and test tubes. Prominent signs throughout the complex remind staff to step into disinfectant footbaths to remove germs from their footwear and to use the hand dispenser to disinfect their hands before entering different zones of the complex.

THE TARGET HATCHERY IS TYPICAL OF THE DOZENS OF SALMON hatcheries in British Columbia. Some are owned by salmon-farming companies to produce their own stock. Most, however, are owned and operated by Fisheries and Oceans Canada (DFO) or community groups that raise salmon for release into the wild, to enhance or help restore marginal salmon runs, or to improve commercial and sport fishing opportunities.

There are many different hatchery layouts, but all use large tanks to raise fish.

PHOTO courtesy B.C. Salmon Farmers Association

Typical troughs (foreground) and circular tanks for raising fry and smolts.

PHOTO courtesy Target Marine

Regardless of ownership, hatcheries all serve the same purpose: to raise fish from the egg stage until they are ready to be released into the wild or transferred into saltwater netpens to be raised by salmon farmers. Government and community support for wild salmon enhancement is well established, and all hatcheries operate using the same processes, so there has been little public criticism of salmon-farm hatcheries.

However, there is growing concern about the practice of intentionally raising and releasing fish into the wild. Salmon raised in hatcheries do not have to compete for survival as their wild counterparts do, and the huge numbers of hatchery-raised fish released into the wild every year may be watering down the genetic uniqueness of wild stocks. Escaped farmed fish may have other effects on wild stocks as well. (For more on escapes, see Chapter 9.)

BROODSTOCK BEGINNINGS

Raising salmon in captivity begins with (or, one could say, ends with) eggs. In the early years of salmon farming, those eggs came from surplus at DFO hatcheries. Later, salmon farmers began to produce their own eggs from the Pacific salmon they were raising.

Between the mid-1980s and mid-1990s, when B.C. salmon farmers began raising Atlantic salmon, they obtained their eggs from Europe. Countries such as Norway and Scotland had already been breeding Atlantic salmon for many years and were producing what were considered "better" stock. However, since 1996, no eggs have been imported from Europe, partly because imported eggs may carry exotic diseases that could harm both farmed and wild salmon. Today, the industry reports that almost all Pacific and Atlantic salmon eggs used by B.C. farmers are obtained from the farmers' own fish. These are known as broodstock.

At a typical farm, a certain number of fish are raised specifically to provide milt (sperm) and eggs for the next generation. Superior specimens are chosen, on the theory that their offspring will also be superior. They are generally selected using one of two methods.

The first method is to select the fastest growing, largest, healthiest fish in the grow-out pens as they mature and to keep them in separate broodstock pens until they are ready to spawn. This process is

63

A hatchery "spawn" crew
collects ripe females from
the broodstock tanks.

PHOTO courtesy Target Marine

similar to the way a rancher selects bulls, a horse breeder picks studs or a crop farmer chooses seed for the following year's stock.

The second method is to tag individual family groups through several generations and monitor them throughout their life to select not only the best males and females, but the best growing pairs.

Both Atlantic and Pacific salmon are genetically programmed to spawn in fall or early winter. About three months before the broodstock are ready to spawn, all of the females, and sometimes the males, are individually injected by hand with an antibiotic to help them better survive the freshwater environment and the stress of being kept in tanks over the next few months. About two months before the broodstock are ready to spawn, they are transported live from the grow-out site to holding tanks at the hatchery or brood site, where the males and females are kept separate. At this stage, the salmon have stopped feeding and won't be fed again. They are monitored closely until their eggs are ripe. Once ready, there is a window of about a week during which the eggs can be taken and fertilized successfully. The milt from the males remains viable for a month or more.

The females' eggs don't all ripen at the same time, so once or twice a week, the spawn crew collect the ripe females and enough males to fertilize their eggs.

Genetically Modified Salmon

In transgenic technology, genetic material from one species is introduced into the genes of another in order to improve crops and animals in ways that are impossible using traditional selection and breeding techniques. Transgenic crops figure significantly in North American agriculture. As of 2005, millions of hectares were planted with transgenic crops in Canada alone.

The federal government has done some experiments at its West Vancouver laboratory, but the B.C. salmon-farming industry has repeatedly claimed that it does not plan to use transgenic fish now or in the future. According to a B.C. Salmon Farmers Association policy statement, "There are no genetically engineered (GE) fish currently allowed for commercial use or release in Canada, nor has any federal department received an application to import or grow GE fish."

However, according to a *Seattle Post-Intelligencer* article in March 2005, an American company has spent the past nine years trying to get its genetically modified salmon approved by the U.S. Food and Drug Administration (FDA) and expects a decision in 2006. Permits to sell and raise the fish could be approved about a decade later. Aqua Bounty Technologies estimates that by using its genetically modified fish, farmers can grow salmon from egg to harvest in about half the time it currently takes. The company says that these fish will be sterilized so that they cannot reproduce in the wild, preventing any adverse effects of mating with wild salmon. As with any genetically modified species, concerns have been raised about the unknown impacts of changing the genetics of fish and creating what some have called "Frankenfish."

Should GM species ever come into use, the manufacture and import of these fish would be regulated under the *Canadian Environmental Assessment Act.*

HARVESTING THE EGGS

Once the females are selected, they are cut open and their eggs are removed by hand. The female carcass and eggs are kept separate. A prime female coho produces 5,000 to 6,000 eggs, and Atlantic salmon, which have smaller eggs, produce about 10,000 to 14,000 eggs.

Before any eggs are used, the females are screened for disease. Screening is not required by law, but considering the costs associated with raising fish, it is in the economic interests of the salmon farm to start with eggs that are 100 percent pathogen-free. The farm's fish-health technician takes several samples of organs and tissues from each female carcass and sends them to a laboratory to test for a number of bacterial pathogens that could be transmitted from parents to eggs. Some of the simpler tests can be done in-house at the larger hatcheries.

If the analysis shows the presence of pathogens, the hatchery crew destroys the eggs from that female. If the tests show viral pathogens, which are not passed down from parents to eggs, the eggs are disinfected. Meanwhile, an appropriate number of males are removed from another tank. Between 5 and 15 mL (1–3 tsp) of milt is collected from each male and examined under a microscope to make sure it contains active sperm. Not all of the male carcasses are screened for disease, because virus and bacteria cells are much larger than sperm cells and will not be able to enter the sperm.

Typically, from 1 to 10 percent of the eggs are destroyed because of the presence of pathogens.

FERTILIZATION AND INCUBATION

In the hatchery's incubation buildings, the milt from one or more males is mixed manually into each pail of eggs. Only one sperm will enter each egg, and when sperm from more than one male is used, the male with the "strongest" sperm will be much more likely to fertilize most of the eggs. Some hatcheries match sperm from specific males to specific batches of eggs; others mix eggs and sperm randomly to aid in maintaining genetic diversity and to ensure that the fittest fish will dominate.

Once the milt is mixed with the eggs, fresh water is stirred into the mixture to activate the sperm. Fertilization takes only about a minute. The eggs are then rinsed and poured into incubation trays (known as Heath stacks) or specialized incubation tanks (known as combi-tanks). To remove any surface bacteria and viruses, the trays or tanks are filled with a disinfectant such as Ovadine, an iodine-based product, that is approved for use on food fish by Health Canada and the U.S. Food and Drug Administration (FDA). The eggs are soaked for exactly 10 minutes to maximize the effectiveness of the disinfectant. The eggs are then flushed with fresh water and left to incubate in the Heath stacks or combi-tanks. These trays and tanks are

Eggs are stripped from a female Atlantic salmon.

PHOTO Peter A. Robson

The hatchery's vet or fish-health technician takes organ and tissue samples, which are tested for pathogens.

PHOTO Peter A. Robson

Milt is collected from a male Atlantic salmon.

PHOTO Peter A. Robson

Milt is examined under a microscope to make sure it is viable.

PHOTO Peter A. Robson

The fertilized eggs are placed into Heath stacks and soaked in disinfectant.

PHOTO Peter A. Robson

Milt from several males is mixed with the eggs of a single female.

PHOTO Peter A. Robson

The fertilized eggs are placed into stacks, where a constant flow of fresh water brings oxygen to the eggs as they develop.

PHOTO courtesy Target Marine

designed to mimic nature by allowing fresh water to upwell through the eggs to provide a supply of aerated water in the same way stream water upwells through naturally spawned eggs buried in gravel.

About 24 hours after fertilization, the eggs are inspected, and any unfertilized eggs that have died and turned milky are removed.

One of the threats to salmon eggs during the incubation process is fungus, which, when present, usually starts forming on dead eggs. Once established, it can spread like a mat to living eggs and destroy them. The agents that cause fungus occur naturally in the creek water that supplies many hatcheries. Those hatcheries that have access to it prefer to use ground water from wells, which is less likely to contain contaminants. Operations that use creek water attempt to filter out any organisms, or they treat the water with a fungicidal agent such as Formalin, which is dripped into the incubation water for a few minutes every few days. In this application, the solution is strong enough to kill the fungus but not strong enough to harm the eggs. Formalin is approved for use on food fish by Health Canada and the U.S. FDA and, according to the manufacturer, degrades to harmless formic acid in the environment.

For many decades, an anti-fungal agent known as malachite green was used at government, community and salmon-farm hatcheries in B.C. and around the world. Malachite green has not been used in the salmon-farming industry since the early 1990s, but traces of the chemical have recently been found in both farmed and wild salmon. (For more on the edibility of farmed salmon, see Chapter 10.)

In the next stage of the incubation process, the eggs become "eyed"—the eyes of the developing salmon become visible through the translucent skin of their eggs. Depending on the species and the temperature of the incubation water, this occurs between 20 and 90 days after fertilization. Hatchery staff can adjust the timing of the eyed stage by changing the temperature of the incubation water. It costs more to heat the water, which adds to the cost of producing the fish, but hatcheries and farms time these processes to take advantage of markets (see sidebar "It's All In the Timing").

Once the eggs have reached the eyed stage, they are re-inventoried so that managers have a more accurate count of the eggs. After handling, the eggs are again soaked in disinfectant.

ALEVINS AND FRY

Once the eggs have become eyed, it takes about a month for the fish to hatch, depending on water temperature. Most of the fish hatch within two or three days of each other. The newborns, known as alevins, feed off their egg sacs until the sacs are absorbed. This takes about a month, again depending on water temperature. During this stage the alevins remain in their incubation trays or combi-tanks, usually in dim light or darkness.

Once the alevins have absorbed their egg sacs, they become free-swimming salmon fry. If they are Pacific salmon, which are more hardy than Atlantic salmon, they are transferred to outdoor tanks or troughs. At this stage, chinook and coho fry weigh less than 0.2 grams (0.007 oz) and measure about 1.5 centimetres (⅝ in) in length. In about six weeks they grow to 3 or 4 grams (0.1–0.14 oz) and measure 8 to 10 cm (3–4 in). As they grow in size, workers move them into increasingly larger tanks to maintain optimum densities.

Atlantic salmon fry are smaller than Pacific and grow much more slowly. They are also less hardy and typically remain in the combitanks until they weigh 3 or 4 grams (0.1–0.14 oz), which takes about six months. Artificial light and warmer water can be used to speed up the process. At this point the fish are moved to larger indoor or outdoor tanks.

About half the hatcheries in B.C. raise Atlantic salmon fry to the smolt stage in indoor recirculating tanks. With such a closed system, the hatchery can produce larger fry of a more uniform size by maintaining optimal conditions. The recirculating filtration system removes any contaminants and pathogens and allows salmon farmers to conserve water—especially important during dry summer weather, when

It's All In the Timing

All salmon—wild and farmed—are genetically programmed to spawn in fall or early winter. Hatcheries could raise their fish according to those natural life cycles, so that the population would smolt and then mature in the netpens in summer and fall. But that is when wild fish mature and migrate back to coastal waters, where many are caught in commercial fisheries. If the production from salmon farms and the commercial harvest coincided, the market would be flooded, prices would plummet and salmon farming would be much less viable.

The market niche captured by the salmon-farming industry is consumer demand for a steady, reliable supply of fresh fish throughout the year. The most efficient way to achieve this is to regulate the growth of smolts by manipulating light and water temperature at the hatchery, because it is much more difficult to affect growth in the saltwater environment.

Hatcheries gear their timing to marketing requirements. The people who market the product determine when and how many fish they will be able to sell to their customers, and the schedule for raising fish is set by working backwards from there. Meeting those projections begins at the hatchery.

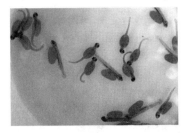

Once hatched, the alevins feed off their egg sacs for about a month, until the sacs are absorbed.

PHOTO courtesy Target Marine

Pacific salmon fry, which are hardier than Atlantic salmon fry, are often raised in outdoor troughs such as these.

PHOTO courtesy Target Marine

surface water sources can dry up. As well, fish raised indoors are protected from stresses caused by birds and other predators, which can cause outdoor fish to go off their feed for several days.

In a typical indoor system, the water is constantly heated, recirculated and filtered. Lights are installed above the tanks to control daylight, depending on when the fish are to be placed in their saltwater grow-out sites. For example, the fry may be subjected to six or seven weeks of 12 hours per day of light, which mimics winter, then six weeks of 24 hours per day of light to mimic summer. This way, the fish reach the smolt stage in a year—about half the time it would take in outside tanks. As well, the fish can grow to 70–120 grams (2.5–4 oz) in weight and 20 cm (8 in) in length when they smolt—at least double the size of the average Pacific salmon when it smolts. The larger the smolts are when released into netpens, the better their chance of survival.

This method is not as cost-effective when farming Pacific salmon, because strong smolts can be grown just as well using natural light conditions.

Regardless of the species, some individuals get more food and grow faster than others. To give smaller individuals a chance to feed, operators grade and sort the fry as many as half a dozen times during their life at the hatchery to keep fish of similar sizes together. The smallest fish are culled.

Land-Based Finfish Aquaculture Waste Control Regulations

Any industrial activity that discharges waste into our oceans deserves scrutiny, and all hatcheries that use more than 75 litres (20 gal) of groundwater per second (as is the case for most hatcheries) are subject to environmental assessment under the *Canadian Environmental Assessment Act*. As well, all hatcheries must be licensed and all discharges must comply with the provincial Ministry of Environment's Land Based Finfish Aquaculture Waste Control Regulations and the hatchery's waste permit. Culls, mortalities and infected eggs must be collected in plastic mort bins and composted.

The runoff from hatcheries consists primarily of stream or well water that has passed through the incubation trays, troughs, tubs and tanks. It also contains fish feces and uneaten feed. Runoff is typically directed into central concrete troughs or pipes and then into a settling tank or pond designed to allow solids to drop out of the waste water. The waste water then flows through pipes to a filtering wetland, where it can decompose in a natural biological action, or to an offshore outfall. This outfall is usually a T-shaped pipe with holes drilled along its length, similar to those used in household septic systems and designed to spread the discharge over a wide area. Waste control regulations are formulated to ensure that any disinfectants and fungicides used at the hatchery are effectively degraded and assimilated by the time they reach the ocean.

The systems used at hatcheries are similar to the primary treatment systems used by cities such as Vancouver to filter human sewage and runoff into the ocean, though obviously cities produce much higher volumes of waste than hatcheries do.

Until the early 2000s, under the Land Based Finfish Aquaculture Waste Control Regulations, hatcheries monitored their waste water by taking samples at the time of year when the biomass of fish being raised was largest, and sending them to the Ministry of Environment. MOE then tested the sample for pH, total suspended solids, dissolved nitrates, ammonia nitrate, and phosphorus and other conditions. In an effort to deregulate the industry, waste-water testing was made the responsibility of the hatchery, with spot-checking by MOE officials to verify compliance.

SMOLTS

All salmon, whether wild or hatchery raised, undergo a natural transformation when they move from the freshwater to the saltwater life stage. The process, called smolting, begins with a change in the appearance of the fish. The mottled parr marks that help camouflage fry in the gravel of a wild stream are replaced by a silver burnish, and scales begin to form to protect the salmon in the ocean. The kidney and gill functions of the salmon also change, in order to deal with salt ions in salt water. Hatchery staff watch the smolting process very carefully. If the smolts are transferred to salt water before they are completely ready, they will not survive. If they are not transferred to salt water soon enough after they have smolted (about two weeks), they will change back to fry. Hatchery staff use several tests to determine whether the fish are ready. One indicator is that the fish begin swimming with the current instead of swimming against it, as they've been doing since hatching. This reflects their natural instinct to head downstream to salt water.

Just prior to reaching the smolt stage, fry are vaccinated against specific pathogens that they may be exposed to in the saltwater environment. One of two methods is used: needle injection or bath treatment. In needle injection, the fish is anaesthetized, then examined and injected by hand. Small and deformed fish are culled. Atlantic salmon and most chinook are vaccinated this way. Bath treatments are generally only used on coho salmon (about 2–3 percent of farmed salmon raised in B.C.), which do not need to be protected against as many bacteria as the other species. The fry are dipped twice in a bath containing the vaccine. As with human vaccination, these treatments are not known to compromise fish health.

When hatchery staff have determined that the smolting process is complete, the fish are counted again, either by hand or by passing through an electronic counting station. At this point they weigh 20–100 grams (0.7–3.5 oz) depending on the species and the hatchery strategy.

The smolts are then transported to the farm site where they will grow to maturity. They are loaded into specialized live-haul barges or ships. As the vessel begins its journey to the grow-out site, salt water is gradually introduced into the holds. By the time the smolts arrive at the fish farm, they are able to survive in the saltwater environment.

By timing the growth of the fish at the hatchery and their placement in saltwater pens, a salmon farming company can harvest market-size fish all year round.

All salmon undergo smolting, a series of physical and physiological changes that enables them to survive the transition from fresh water to salt water. Parr marks are replaced by a silver burnish, and scales begin to form.

PHOTO Peter Chettleburgh

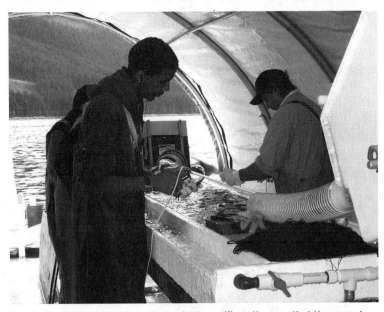

Vaccination helps protect smolts against specific pathogens that they may be exposed to in the saltwater environment.

PHOTO Peter Chettleburgh

All-Female Salmon

In the wild, each river has its own genetically unique salmon stocks that have developed over thousands of years to return to that specific river. A certain percentage of the males in any given stock are predisposed to mature sexually and return to their home river to spawn a year before the others—a process known as jacking. This is nature's way of preventing inbreeding within a particular stock and year class. When the eggs of another year class are fertilized, new genetic material is brought into the mix.

Jacking takes place in the salmon-farm environment, as in nature. Before the rest of the population reach harvest size, a percentage of the fish become darker as they begin to mature sexually, and their flesh softens as the energy used to grow larger is redirected into making sperm. At this point they lose their commercial value. If 10 percent of the males in a population were to jack, they could make the difference between profit and loss. There is no way for salmon farmers to prevent jacking, or to predict which fish will jack.

One solution is to produce all female fish, which then mature as males with viable sperm, then mate with regular females to produce all female offspring. The technique is used with most if not all of the chinook and a portion of the coho salmon raised in B.C. By 2005, the technology for producing all-female populations of Atlantic salmon had not been developed.

IN WILD SALMON-SPAWNING CREEKS AND RIVERS, THERE IS NO WAY to control the spread of naturally occurring pathogens, or to limit their impact. However, through pre-screening eggs, filtrating water supplies, maintaining biosecurity and constantly observing the eggs and fish, there is considerably less chance for hatchery-raised fish to carry pathogens than wild fish. In any case, it is not in the economic interests of salmon farmers to raise unhealthy fish, a fact that works to protect the aquatic environment.

THE NETPENS

The Spartan aluminum workboat races across whitecapped waves, slamming and rolling as it makes its way to the salmon farm. Inside the cabin the roar and throb of the engine is so loud that the two employees have to shout to make themselves heard.

The scenery outside is a magnificent maze of rocks, small islets and heavily treed hills stretching up into the distance. The dark blue waters are clear and pristine. Two eagles circle in the distance. Other than the occasional logging scar, there are few signs of human habitation.

Suddenly, as the workboat rounds a point of land, the salmon-farm complex comes into view. It consists of a large square of floating grey walkways, massive round anchor buoys and a substantial two-storey forest green building. Along the walkways are two parallel rows of eight pens. Each pen measures about 1,000 square metres (1,300 sq yd) in area and is surrounded by metal railings and shrouded with light netting.

The ground floor of the main building is stacked floor to ceiling with dozens and dozens of shrink-wrapped pallets containing white plastic sacks of fish feed. There is a faint fishy smell in the air. One part of the warehouse is walled off and contains a room with microscopes and a variety of lab equipment; another contains assorted tools and machinery in various stages of repair. The hum of a generator comes from a shed on a second, smaller barge tied up to the main barge.

The second floor of the main building contains living quarters with a big, open living room and kitchen, half a dozen small bedrooms and a large washroom/shower room. In another room a computer hums, and stacks of documents and other papers fill every inch of desk space. The living quarters are rustic and the furniture is well worn. A TV connected to a satellite dish blares away unwatched as two of the farm crew banter with the newly arrived workboat crew. Outside in the netpens, the occasional salmon leaps up, breaks the surface and splashes lightly as it lands.

A typical salmon farm consists of 8 to 12 individual square netpens, each measuring 33×33 metres (108×108 ft). The pens are hung on galvanized steel walkways supported by foam-filled polyethylene floats. Most farms arrange their pens in a rectangle two pens wide,

A typical farm in the mid-2000s, with pens, housing, feed shed and generator building.

though some companies are finding that if they stack single-wide pens lengthwise, there is better water flow through the pens and less waste buildup under the pen.

The nets are constructed of knotless nylon to reduce abrasion damage to the fish. A typical net measures 20 metres (65 ft) deep on the sides and 30 metres (100 ft) at the bottom centre. The mesh size varies depending on whether the salmon are smolts or adults. Typically, smaller-volume netpens are used to rear broodstock. At most farms, an extra layer of larger-mesh net is hung around the perimeter and under the farm, forming a complete enclosure, to keep predators away from the main netpens.

The cage system and its nets and anchors are engineered to hold the farm permanently aligned in one position—usually perpendicular to the prevailing currents. The system must be able to withstand the forces of the most extreme currents, wind, waves and tidal fluctuations expected at the site—and then some. The task grows more challenging as salmon farmers locate their operations in deeper (often 100 metres/328 ft or more) and more exposed waters, where the flushing action of stronger currents (1 to 3 knots) reduces and often eliminates waste buildup under the farm site.

Electrical power is usually provided by diesel generators, and water comes from an adjacent stream. In remote areas, food, fuel and sometimes water are brought in on the feed-supply vessel every week or two.

SMOLT STOCKS

Salmon farms are typically stocked with smolts over a period of a month or more, in fall or spring and depending on the company's management strategy and hatchery production schedule. Each batch of smolts is a slightly different size to ensure a steady supply of fresh salmon. One smolt costs about $2, so salmon farmers have a strong financial incentive to nurture their stocks.

A salmon-farm site is usually empty when the first smolts arrive, and will have been empty for some months prior to stocking to eliminate any pathogens that may have appeared among the previous population. This practice is known as breaking the disease cycle.

As well, smolts are not placed on farms that contain adult fish, because there is a chance that pathogens carried by adults—even healthy adults—can be transferred to the younger fish. This practice is known as separating year classes.

Once the smolts arrive at the farm site, they are placed in smolt pens with a mesh size of ½–¾ inch (1–2 cm) square. The mesh is small enough to prevent the smallest smolts from escaping, yet large enough to allow currents to flow easily through the net. Depending on the farm, fish are placed directly into full-size pens fitted with small-mesh nets, or placed in smaller smolt nets suspended within the full-size pens, or placed in full-size small-mesh pens fitted with one or more mesh dividers.

At a larger farm, a pen can be about 15,000 cubic metres (19,500 cu yd) in volume and can hold 35,000 to 60,000 fish. Such a farm can raise 250,000 to 1,000,000 fish at one time, depending on the size and number of netpens, the species, the size of the fish and the company's optimum stocking density. Farmed salmon are typically stocked at densities of 5–13 kilograms per cubic metre (8½–22 lbs/cu yd). If the fish have too much room, the company won't realize the full potential of its netcages. If the fish are too crowded, they will have to compete harder for feed, and the stress associated with crowding may make them more susceptible to sickness and infection.

The first few months at the farm is the time when the most natural mortality occurs among the smolts. The ones that don't survive are typically individuals that have not smolted properly, or for some reason cannot compete successfully for feed and starve to death. Smolts are also often more susceptible to becoming sick. Unlike wild fish, which have been exposed to a range of pathogens since the egg

Live-haul boats are typically used to transfer smolts to the salmon-farm site. Helicopters are used on occasion.

PHOTO courtesy Target Marine

A smaller-mesh net for smolts is often hung inside the full-size net until the salmon reach a certain size.

PHOTO Peter A. Robson

stage, they have not had the chance to build up resistance to naturally occurring marine pathogens. Still, the mortality rate of smolts is considerably less than 1 percent.

Smolts that start out in small-mesh pens stay there until they grow to about 700 grams (24 oz) and 30 centimetres (12 in) in length. This can take anywhere from three to six months, depending on the species, environmental conditions and stocking size. Population density in the pens increases as they grow. For smolts that start out in full-size pens, a larger mesh net (1–1½ inches/2.5–3.8 cm square) is placed around the small-mesh net, and the small-mesh net is then removed. Fish that were kept in a smaller pen suspended in the large pen can simply spill into the full-size pen. When the fish must be transferred between netpens, there are two ways of doing so. The least stressful method is to employ divers to sew a mesh tunnel between the cages and to swim the fish into the new pen. The other method is to transfer the fish with mechanical pumps.

Salmon eat more and grow faster during the summer months, largely because there is more daylight. Underwater lights are used at some farms to artificially extend "daylight," so that the fish will continue the heavier summer feeding regime into fall and winter, and grow faster. Lights are expensive—the capital costs of equipment, wiring and electricity are considerable. But the use of lights can shorten the time it takes for fish to reach market size by about half—from two years to one year.

Concerns have been raised that fish-farm lights attract other fish, such as juvenile salmon, herring and eulachon, which become free food for the fish inside the netpens. Small fish do not commonly swim into schools of carnivorous fish, but it does happen. Farm staff, who spend most of their work days feeding and monitoring the salmon with underwater cameras, report that they sometimes see small fish swimming about in a netpen and that the salmon don't appear to pay any attention to them. This may be because farmed fish constantly have full bellies and are conditioned all their lives to eat pellets. Staff also report that when adult salmon are harvested, they sometimes find a few fish that must have swum into the cage when they were small, then stayed on to feed and grow and eventually became too large to exit the cage. It doesn't appear that farmed salmon are having any effect on populations of other small fish, but no extensive studies have been undertaken.

The use of lights has also been compared with the commercial herring fishing technique known as pit-lamping. Fishermen would seek out a school of herring at night, then turn on bright lights and quietly drift or anchor above the school. The lights would bring the herring to the surface and the fishermen would then set their nets around the school. It was so effective and so widespread that fisheries managers became worried that herring stocks would collapse, and the practice was banned more than 30 years ago. Pit-lamping differed from the use of night lights in that the key to its success was to find a large school of herring first. It was not effective for fishermen to pick a random location, turn the lights on and wait for the jackpot. Schools of fish such as herring have never been observed to school up under salmon farms.

PREDATOR CONTROL

A netcage full of healthy captive fish is irresistible to predators. Seals, sea lions, otters, mink, mud sharks (dogfish) and birds such as kingfishers and great blue herons are all known to help themselves to a salmon dinner whenever they can. Predators can cause considerable economic losses to salmon farms by killing stock—seals and sea lions can kill hundreds of fish in a night—and by inflicting wounds that can lower the market value of the fish. Even when the salmon are not harmed, they are severely stressed when predators attack, and that makes them more susceptible to disease.

To protect their investment and to satisfy the requirements of an Aquaculture Licence, salmon farmers must try to prevent marine mammals and birds from preying on farmed fish. Over the years, they have tried a number of measures to address the problem. Bird netting over the pens has largely kept birds from preying on smolts, but other predators are more difficult to deal with.

When a seal or sea lion attacks a netpen, it charges into the net and tries to bite the fish through the mesh. The animal doesn't end up with the whole fish, but sometimes it manages to get a mouthful. Pairs of seals or sea lions are known to work as a team. One spooks the fish from one side of the net. The fish bunch up against the opposite side or dive to the bottom, where the other predator is waiting to charge.

In the early years of salmon farming, it was common for a fish farmer to keep a loaded rifle at hand. Few objections were raised to the practice of shooting predators, which was not unique to aquaculture. Commercial fishermen were shooting hundreds of seals and sea lions that were stealing salmon from their nets and otherwise interfering with their work. But shooting is no longer an acceptable alternative. All of the major salmon-farming companies say that they have prohibited guns at farm sites, though an operator may obtain a special federal permit to take a gun on site and kill a persistent predator that manages to climb into a netpen. The sidebar "Marine Mammals Killed at B.C. Salmon Farms" shows the number of marine mammals killed by salmon farmers since 1993 (earliest figures available), according to their reports to DFO. The table shows a significant decline in reported mammal kills in recent years. Groups opposed to salmon farming point out that these are the reported figures, and say that many more mammals are actually being killed near salmon farms.

At one point, salmon farmers experimented with acoustic deterrent devices (ADDs), which emit a loud underwater noise designed to scare away predators. These were not effective, and whale researchers raised concerns about negative effects on dolphins, porpoises, whales and other animals. ADDs have been banned since 2000, though salmon farms in B.C. say that they stopped using them a few years before that because they didn't work. The biologist Alexandra Morton has said that years after ADDs went out of use, killer whales still avoid the Broughton archipelago. Ted Needham, former director of West Coast operations for Heritage Salmon, responds that killer whale populations have not changed. Because of Morton's strong vocal criticism of the industry, he says, salmon farmers are no longer co-operating with her by reporting whale sightings. There is no scientific data to support either claim. In 2005, however, DFO used an ADD in Gold River in an effort to keep Luna, the infamous friendly killer whale, away from the seaplane docks, where she'd caused damage to local floatplanes. The unit was reportedly effective.

Scaring devices such as seal bombs have also been used, but they have been shown to be better at scaring the fish than deterring predators.

The most successful method so far is the use of predator nets, which are made of heavy mesh and hung like a curtain around the perimeter of a farm. In almost all cases they are sewn to another net (known as a shark net), which hangs below the netcages. Together they form an impenetrable envelope, or second cage, around the salmon farm. The sides and bottom of the net are heavily weighted to keep the nets drum tight. They have a larger mesh size than the nets enclosing the salmon. The mesh is small enough to keep predators out but large enough that water can flow freely through the netpens. These nets successfully deter seals and sea lions, as well as mud sharks, which are known to attack salmon by pushing up from the bottom of the net. The predator net also serves as a second wall, a safety net should any salmon escape from the main net. The downside to predator nets is that they are costly to purchase, and they must be either coated with an anti-fouling substance or cleaned regularly to prevent fouling. Many salmon farmers believe that the benefits clearly outweigh the expense, and about half the salmon farms in

B.C. use predator nets. Those operators report that predators soon learn that there is no free lunch and move on to more productive hunting grounds.

The farms that do not use wraparound predator nets either don't have problems with predators or have installed heavier mesh nets (about two to four times the strength of a standard net) that make it virtually impossible for a predator to punch through to the fish. Some older farms use the heavier nets simply because of farm design—the floats cannot support the heavy predator nets, and the outside walkways are too narrow to allow enough space between the predator net and the main nets.

Otters and mink present different problems. They can climb up out of the water and over the netpen fencing and duck under the bird netting. Salmon farmers say live trapping has proven to be the most effective way to deal with these animals. Once caught, they can be relocated at a distance from the farm. Some farms have installed non-lethal electric fencing around netcages, powered by electricity or solar cells and batteries. The fences are generally only switched on at night, when the farm is quiet and predators are most likely to pay a visit. Operators report that one experience with the electric fence is usually enough to stop a predator from returning.

Between early 2003 and June 2005, according to the Ministry of Agriculture and Lands' Fish Health Database, the average mortality rate of farmed Atlantic salmon in B.C. from predators was 0.08 percent, and the average rate for farmed Pacific salmon was 0.11 percent.

ALGAL BLOOMS

One of the greatest threats to salmon farms is algal blooms, which cause significant losses. When conditions are right, naturally occurring phytoplankton (microscopic plants) reproduce extremely rapidly and discolour the ocean over a large area. There are many species of phytoplankton, and some of them produce toxins that are harmful to other aquatic life. These incidents are known as Harmful Algal Blooms (HABs). Some species of toxic algae can accumulate in filter-feeding bivalves such as oysters, mussels and clams; and fish, birds or mammals (including humans) that consume these bivalves can get sick or die.

Marine Mammals Killed at B.C. Salmon Farms

YEAR	HARBOUR SEALS	CALIFORNIA SEA LIONS	STELLER SEA LIONS	TOTAL KILLS	PERMITS ISSUED
1993	483	14	9	506	88
1994	414	3	3	420	93
1995	577	24	6	607	94
1996	512	57	27	596	117
1997	542	59	37	638	119
1998	391	92	63	546	133
1999	499	147	103	749	138
2000	426	243	49	718	140
2001	298	92	30	420	147
2002	123	20	17	160	150
2003	48	14	3	65	153
2004	120	6	**	126	158
2005*	69	9	**	78	127

* To December 2, 2005
** As of 2004, permit holders are no longer allowed to kill Steller sea lions, as they are listed as a species of special concern by the Committee on the Status of Endangered Wildlife in Canada (COSEWIC).

Certain species of HABs, including the flagellate *Heterosigma akashiwo* and two species of the plankton *Chaetoceros*, are non-toxic and do not affect humans, but are harmful to finfish and are major threats to farmed salmon. Flagellates can poison salmon and diatoms can irritate the gills so severely that the fish produce enough mucus to suffocate.

Most wild fish can simply avoid HABs by swimming around or below them; fish in netpens cannot. When a HAB develops near a salmon farm, or drifts in on the currents, it can kill 90 percent of the population in just a few days. Such episodes can cost a farm millions of dollars in lost revenue. As well, fish that aren't killed are often weakened by the stress, which leaves them more susceptible to illness.

Algal blooms generally develop in waters where nutrients and sunlight provide the energy for phytoplankton to produce new cells.

When temperature, salinity and water column stability are just right, they can reproduce rapidly. The bloom can form offshore and be carried inshore by water currents, or form in a shallow bay or coastal inlet. Once the nutrients are consumed, or environmental conditions change to mix or break up the bloom, the phytoplankton begin to die off. Some form a hard coat and settle to the bottom. If this occurs in shallow areas (about 10 metres/33 ft or less), the phytoplankton can stay alive until light levels, temperature and salinity are such that they can begin to reproduce again. These locations are known as seed areas. Salmon farmers try to avoid siting their farms near seed areas or any spot where algal blooms occur frequently.

In the early years of aquaculture, however, little was known about the harmful effects of certain algal blooms because they are not a problem for wild fish. Salmon farmers had to learn about blooms the hard way, and losses from frequent blooms were one reason that many early fish farmers moved out of the Sunshine Coast area.

Because of the danger of algal blooms, salmon farmers monitor plankton levels daily. Water samples are taken at different levels below the farm and examined under a microscope. The various species are identified and abundance is recorded. This work can provide early warning of an algal bloom.

When a bloom threatens a farm, operators immediately stop feeding the fish, to which the fish respond by settling to the cooler, darker water at the bottom of the pen, away from the top layers of the water column, where blooms are most concentrated. Fish that are not feeding also breathe less deeply and take in less algae-laden water through their gills. The fish don't put on weight, but that is preferable to having them die.

Another measure to protect the fish is to lower tarps as a skirt around the perimeter of the netpen to help keep the phytoplankton out of the pens. The tarps are only effective when the bloom is close to the surface—some blooms extend below the bottom of the tarps. This method reduces the amount of oxygen-rich water that normally flushes through the pens, but that too is better than losing huge numbers of fish.

Some farms install a series of pipes that form a square below and around the perimeter of the netpens. Workers then pump large

This algal bloom in Kyuquot Sound on the west coast of Vancouver Island was caused by the flagellate *Heterosigma akashiwo*.

PHOTO Nicky Haigh

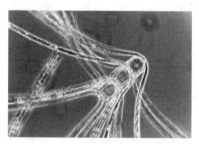

Close-up of the diatom *Chaetoceros concavicorne*, which irritates a salmon's gills, causing extreme mucus production that suffocates the fish.

PHOTO Nicky Haigh

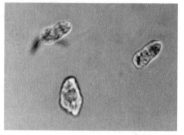

Close-up of the plankton *Heterosigma akashiwo*, a flagellate that can be toxic to salmon.

PHOTO Nicky Haigh

volumes of air down the pipes. The air exits through a series of holes, which creates a bubbling effect around the netpens. Deeper, colder, plankton-free waters are brought to the surface, and the bubbling water acts as a barrier to stop the plankton from moving into the netcages. The disadvantage is that the water upwelled from the depths may have lower levels of dissolved oxygen, which can kill the salmon. The bubbling method is sometimes used in conjunction with tarps.

MORTS

Just as some people die before their time, from disease or accidents, salmon die for a number of reasons whether they live in the wild or in captivity. About 98 percent do not survive the rigours of the ocean to return and spawn. Farmed salmon too can die prematurely from a number of causes, including disease, inability to feed adequately and, to a much lesser extent, predation. Salmon farms monitor mortalities constantly. Losses of 5 to 10 percent of the population over the grow-out cycle are considered acceptable. When disease breaks out or an algal bloom occurs, those numbers can skyrocket.

Farm staff check for slow swimmers (unhealthy fish) and floating carcasses (morts) every day and remove them with dipnets. For many years, salmon farms have experimented with automated mort collection systems in which cones are fitted at the bottom of netpens and pneumatic air pressure is applied to concentrate the morts. These systems have mixed success rates. Most farms have found it more efficient to use contract or staff scuba divers to collect morts once or twice a week, or more often if needed. Between netpens, the diver is sprayed with disinfectant to prevent the spread of any pathogens from one pen to another. The divers wear special vinyl dry suits, which are easier to disinfect than traditional neoprene.

The morts are then emptied into tubs. Because of the frequent removal of morts, most are still firm and can easily be counted and examined by farm staff, who try to determine why they died. If necessary, the fish's belly is slit open and its internal organs are examined. A fish-health technician or veterinarian may be on hand to assist. Once examined, the morts are placed in sealed metal or plastic mort bins, which are often located on a separate float to avoid any transmission of pathogens to other fish.

A diver prepares to dive for morts (dead fish) at a salmon farm in Kyuquot Sound, Vancouver Island.

PHOTO Peter A. Robson

The morts are counted and examined to determine the cause of death.

PHOTO Peter A. Robson

When the totes are full, they must be barged to a licensed land-based mort disposal or recycling facility, where they are composted or used in the manufacture of fertilizers and enriched soils. The composting process generates high enough temperatures to kill any disease pathogens that may be present. Other morts are buried in landfills or incinerated. Some farms make arrangements to ship their fresh (same-day) morts to rendering plants.

When massive losses occur, the morts are removed on barges or fish packers. If the fish have died from disease, the water in which they were transported must be pumped ashore to a landfill or other facility and disinfected.

When the fish have died from algal blooms, the morts may, under emergency permit, be hauled and discharged offshore. In September 2002, when a bloom caused a massive die-off at a salmon farm in Esperanza Inlet and the weight of the dead fish threatened to sink the pens, the company was granted permission to dump some 250,000 fish 30 kilometres (18 mi) off the west coast of Vancouver Island. According to the Georgia Strait Alliance, an environmental group, a week later there was a "3-km-long floating slick of dead, rotting Atlantic salmon."

It is illegal to discharge fish into the aquatic environment when they have died from disease. The disposal of morts falls under the provincial *Waste Management Act* and the Finfish Aquaculture Waste Control Regulations as well as existing DFO and Environment Canada regulations. The salmon-farming industry hasn't always played by the rules. For example, over the years there have been incidents of totes of rotting morts being left to accumulate and sometimes overflow on barges until it was economically feasible to have them moved. However, the Pacific Fisheries Resource Conservation Council, a broad-based, federal government-appointed advisory group, did a study and concluded in its 2002 report, *Making Sense of the Salmon Aquaculture Debate*, that there was no evidence of serious risk to wild fish from morts or current mort disposal procedures.

HARVEST TIME

When farmed salmon have reached market size, they are harvested pen by pen—ideally for the salmon farmer, several times during the year to provide a steady supply of fish to the marketplace.

If a population of farmed salmon has been treated with drugs, any residues must be below maximum allowable levels established by the Canadian Food Inspection Agency (CFIA) before the fish are sold to the public. Salmon farmers meet this requirement by allowing established minimum withdrawal periods for specific drugs. In most cases, this means that the fish cannot be harvested for up to 180 days following treatment. Because most farmed salmon are never treated with any type of drug, this rule only affects a small percentage of the salmon raised in B.C.

Whether or not drugs have been used, farmed salmon are not fed for several days prior to harvest. This ensures that any feed in their stomachs is fully digested and helps to firm up the flesh and reduce waste at the processing plant. When it is time to transport the fish to the plant, they are removed from their pens with large dipnets (brailed) or pumped out of their netcages into a fish packer. Wherever practical, the fish are transported to the processing plant alive in specially modified vessels that supply the fish with a steady

A specialized packer brails salmon from the netpens. The fish will be transported live to the processing plant for maximum freshness.

PHOTOS Ian Douglas

supply of oxygenated water. Believe it or not, the fish can actually become seasick during the voyage.

When the processing plant is too far away, or some other circumstance precludes live transport, the fish may be slaughtered on-board the fish packer and packed in ice or chilled sea water until they arrive at the plant.

When live fish arrive at the processing plant, they are either killed with a pneumatic stunner or placed in a tank containing carbon dioxide, which slows down their metabolism so that they can be handled and bled. They are then placed on conveyor belts and moved into the processing plant.

Depending on the customer, the fish are either processed into fillets and/or other value-added products, or simply sold whole, head off and gutted. Fillets must be kept for two days to allow the flesh to firm up so that the pin-bones can be mechanically removed. Whole fish are usually on store shelves within 24 to 48 hours of slaughter.

Blood Water and Offal

If a plant processes infected farmed or wild salmon, some pathogens can be passed into the environment through blood water (waste water) and offal. When salmon are healthy at harvest, blood water and offal are not of concern. Farmed salmon that have been treated for bacterial diseases cannot be harvested until they are healthy and have eliminated antibiotics from their systems.

The disposal of fish killed by the IHN (infectious hematopoeitic necrosis) virus is of special concern to salmon farmers. (For more on IHN, see Chapter 6.) Although wild fish, most notably sockeye, often carry the virus, they are not known to be affected by it in the saltwater environment. But IHN can be spread to Atlantic salmon in nearby farms, which are very susceptible to the virus. When IHN is present at a salmon farm and the fish are harvested on site, the blood water must be contained and disinfected before it is released into the aquatic environment, or pumped to shoreside disinfecting facilities. Once unloaded, the packer's hold water must be either disinfected within the holds or pumped ashore to a land-based disposal site.

Although not mandatory, all of the farmed salmon processed in B.C. is handled at plants that treat their waste water with ozone or chlorination/dechlorination treatment systems. These methods are designed to be 100 percent effective in killing viral and bacterial pathogens.

All of the major farmed-salmon producers collect their offal—skin, bones, guts and other bits and pieces left over after processing—and ship it off for composting or rendering at the West Coast Reduction plant in Vancouver.

Unlike farmed-salmon waste, the untreated blood water from the wild-fish processing industry is discharged directly into the aquatic environment.

FALLOWING

Once a salmon farm is emptied of its fish, most salmon farmers remove the nets to clean, repair and/or treat them, and to do any necessary maintenance on the farm structures. This work usually takes several months. Some farms are disassembled and towed to new locations. Either way, when the farm is kept free of fish for several months, any pathogens that may still be present eventually die because of the absence of hosts.

Under the new provincial Finfish Aquaculture Waste Control Regulations, samples of the sediment under a salmon farm must be taken before a site is approved for restocking. If those sediments have built up to levels that the ministry deems harmful to the natural biological and chemical balance, the farm cannot be restocked until the makeup of those sediments is restored to acceptable levels (see Chapter 8). For most sites that are deep and well flushed, sediment damage is not a concern. Other sites have to be fallowed for a few weeks or even several months to allow bottom sediments to return to acceptable levels.

NET FOULING AND TREATMENT

Any structure that is immersed in salt water attracts marine plants and animals. Seaweeds, mussels and small crustaceans are quick to attach to floats, anchor lines and nets—especially during the summer months. Even a small boat moored in salt water needs regular attention. The situation is no different at salmon farms. A primary concern in the salmon-farming industry is the marine growth that forms on the nets and reduces current flow through the mesh. When fouling organisms are left to accumulate, they can almost completely block the water exchange and become so heavy that it is impossible to remove the nets without tearing them.

To address this, most operators treat their nets with a latex-based anti-fouling treatment, similar to standard boat-bottom paint but with only half as much copper—enough to discourage marine growth but not enough to be toxic to the fish in the netpens. Typically, copper-treated nets are removed at the end of each growing cycle and taken to a shore-based washing and re-treating facility. Some years ago, nets were removed, cleaned and treated on site, but this is no longer allowed, partly because of concerns about the impact of sudden pulses of copper into the environment and the potential buildup of mussels and other aquatic creatures washed off the nets onto the sea floor.

B.C.'s largest net-cleaning company, Wavemaster Inc., and similar smaller companies clean and treat about 80 percent of the nets used by the salmon-farming industry in B.C. At Wavemaster's facility in Campbell River, nets are first dried under cover to kill any marine

Anything immersed in salt
water, including a salmon-farm
net, soon attracts marine plants
and animals.

PHOTO Ian Douglas

growth. They are then washed in a giant drum washing machine
measuring 7.2 by 3 metres (24 by 10 feet). When clean, they are transported to a nearby net loft, where they are examined, repaired as
required and tested for strength (nets must meet minimum strength
standards as a condition of an Aquaculture Licence). They are then
returned to Wavemaster and dipped into a tank containing the anti-
fouling solution. Wavemaster's operation is self-contained. The drum
and tanks are built on concrete pads identical to those used to contain oil tanks. Any runoff and waste-washing water is directed into
a concrete settling pond and then recycled.

About 20 percent of the nets used in B.C. are not treated with
anti-fouling. Marine growth builds up much faster on these nets
than it does on treated nets, so they are washed in position several
times during the grow-out phase. Because most fouling occurs close
to the surface, where sunlight aids in the growth of seaweeds, farms
can discourage growth to some extent by lifting portions of the nets
out of the water on a regular, rotating basis. When these parts are
allowed to dry in the open air, the growth is killed and washes off
when the net is lowered back into the water. For the deeper portions
of the net, divers use high-pressure hoses to remove the growth as
required. As with treated nets, untreated nets are removed at the end
of the grow-out cycle, cleaned and tested.

Companies that choose not to treat their nets do so for a combination of reasons. Cost is one factor. Anti-fouling treatments cost $2,000 to $12,000 per net. As well, although the CFIA has never found farmed salmon to contain unsafe levels of copper, much public concern to the contrary has been expressed. For this reason, companies that can tell their customers that the fish were raised in pens without anti-fouling treatment may have a slight advantage in marketing their fish.

The Cost of Farming Salmon

The capital cost to build a salmon-farm structure is between $1 and $3 million. Once built, the farm has to be stocked. A farm that holds one million smolts must spend $1.5 to $2 million to raise those smolts. It costs about $7 million more to feed those fish during the grow-out cycle. The operator must also pay for staffing, maintenance, fuel, veterinarians, divers and administration, which brings the total cost of raising 900,000 fish (assuming a natural mortality of 10 percent) to $10–$13 million. Should the farm be hit by an uncontrollable breakout of the IHN virus or a significant algal bloom, half or more of the population may die.

But if everything goes well for the salmon farmer, those 900,000 fish will go to market as 5.5 million kilograms (6,000 tons) of product. Assuming the company can get about $3 per kilogram for those fish, it would realize a return of $13.5 million. With strong competition from other farmed-salmon-producing countries, margins are narrow and B.C. salmon farmers say that a price change of less than 50 cents in the marketplace can make or break that multimillion-dollar investment. When something goes wrong, losses can quickly run into the millions of dollars.

Considering the amount of money involved, it isn't surprising that the industry is dominated by large multinational companies.

5

FOOD FOR THOUGHT

Salmon-Farm Feeds

Feeding time at the farm. Note the pellets.

Food pellets hiss and clank as the powerful air pump blows them from a large hopper in the feed warehouse, out a manifold and out along pipes running the length of the farm walkways. They whoosh out of a feeder pipe, hit a deflector plate fitted on its end, and spray fan-like into one of the pens. The splash of the feed is a sentinel to the farmed salmon and the normally still waters boil as the fish chase after the pellets. A farm worker peers into a wheeled, pulpit-like unit containing a TV screen. It is connected to an upward-facing underwater camera hung about 10 metres (33 ft) deep from a pulley in the middle of the pen. On screen, the fish can be seen twisting and lunging for the pellets, which are clearly visible as they sink slowly. The process goes on for 40 minutes, during which time the worker uses a hand-held remote control unit to adjust the delivery of feed to match the activity of the fish. As the fish become satiated, they swim more slowly and drop deeper into the pen. The feeder is shut off once the pellets begin to fall past the level of the camera. The worker wheels the TV unit to the next pen and the process begins again.

FOR SALMON-FARM STAFF, FEEDING THE FISH TAKES THE BETTER PART of every day. Most farms have computerized feeding programs that calculate the optimum amount of feed for each pen based on the size of the fish, expected growth rates and a variety of feeding regimes. However, in the end, proper feeding comes down to the experience of the staff who are actually on the walkways monitoring and controlling the feeding operation.

A staff member observes fish feeding through an underwater camera and uses remote controls to adjust the amount of feed being delivered. Feeding farmed salmon takes the better part of every day.

PHOTO Peter A. Robson

A number of factors affect the feeding regimes and appetite of the population. They include energy requirements, diet, behaviour, stress, health, age, water temperature and other environmental conditions. Generally, the fish feed more in the summer, when they are more active, hungry and likely to undergo most of their annual growth.

At peak feeding times in the summer, a large farm can go through 15–18 tonnes (16.5–20 tons) of feed daily. At about $1,200 per tonne, it can cost over $20,000 per day; therefore salmon farmers keep a close eye on feed conversion ratios (FCRs), which represent the number of kilograms of feed it takes to produce 1 kilogram (2.2. lbs) of growth in the fish.

The use of cameras and farmers' growing knowledge about feeding regimes has improved FCRs over the past decade or so by reducing the amount of waste feed by half. Even without these improvements, fish are among the most efficient of all farmed animals in feed conversion. The average FCR in the salmon-farming industry is about

1.2:1, compared with about 5:1 for grain-fed beef cattle, 5:1 for pork and 2:1 for chicken. This is partly because fish are cold blooded and don't have to expend energy to heat themselves. Nor do they have to spend a lot of energy building a bone structure to support them against gravity, as land animals do.

In salmon farming, as in all agricultural industries that raise animals intensively, feeds are specially formulated to produce maximum growth rates in as short a period as possible. Unlike many farmed animals, though, salmon are carnivorous—they require feeds that contain animal proteins and oils. Historically, those ingredients came mostly from small fish caught in commercial fisheries off South America. The use of wild fish to feed farmed fish has raised concerns about the impact on those wild stocks, as well as the potential effects of this feed on other fish and organisms that come into contact with them.

CARNIVORES, HERBIVORES AND OMNIVORES

Between 80 and 85 percent of all of the fish raised in aquaculture operations around the world are raised mostly on vegetable-based feeds. Freshwater fish such as carp can digest and assimilate the complex carbohydrates produced by plants. Catfish are omnivores, so they can process both plant and animal proteins and they require only small amounts of animal protein in their food.

The remaining 15 to 20 percent of fish raised in aquaculture are primarily carnivorous. Salmonids (as well as all of the commercial freshwater trout raised in North America) represent about half of the carnivorous species raised in aquaculture. Other species include tuna, eel, halibut, cod and sablefish. Carnivorous fish cannot effectively digest and assimilate the complex carbohydrates in plant matter. They require proteins, fatty acids and oils that can be had only by eating other animals.

All animals must convert food to protein. The growth of any animal, whether carnivorous, omnivorous or non-carnivorous, is "subsidized" by land-based or aquatic ecosystems, so there is an ecological cost to farming any of them.

The reason carnivorous fish are cultured is because there is a market for them. Most North Americans simply prefer salmon over carp and other fish. If there were not a market for salmon above what was already being supplied by commercial salmon fisheries, there would be no salmon-farming industry. British Columbia's climate and its extensive, well-flushed waterway are much better suited to culturing salmon than non-carnivorous fish.

Ocean Ranching in Alaska

Wild fish are used in the manufacture of fish feed, and they are also consumed by the 5 billion hatchery-raised salmon and sea-run trout released into the wild every year by Pacific Rim countries (including Canada). To calculate the amount of natural prey eaten by hatchery-raised fish when released into the wild, William Waknitz, a research biologist with the U.S. National Marine Fisheries Service, studied Alaska's ocean-ranching program.

Alaska's wild salmon stocks are healthy, and the state's hatchery programs operate only to provide additional salmon for harvest by commercial fishermen. Each year the state releases about 1.5 billion salmon, which have been raised in exactly the same manner as farmed salmon. They are fed the same feed and they spend up to half their lives in captivity. The only difference is that they are released as juvenile salmon. In 2000, those hatcheries produced 63 million returning salmon, in a process known as ocean ranching.

It is generally accepted among marine biologists that it takes 5–15 kilograms (11–33 lbs) of natural prey to produce 1 kilogram (2.2 lbs) of salmon. Based on the lowest estimate (5 kg/11 lbs) and an average weight per fish at return of 1.8 kg (4 lbs), it takes 567,000 tonnes (510,300 tons) of natural prey to support Alaska's hatchery releases. "If those fish had never been released," wrote Waknitz, "the food they subsequently consumed would have been available for wild salmon and other species. So the natural organisms eaten by Alaska hatchery salmon constitute a man-made ecological cost just as surely as the salmon feed eaten by farmed fish."

Waknitz calculated that when the fish released from enhancement hatcheries in B.C., Washington and Oregon are added to the mix, the ecological cost to the ocean biomass rises by about 25 percent, to 756,000 tonnes (680,400 tons). Scientists have long been aware that the ocean can only provide a limited amount of feed and when demand outstrips supply, a proportional number of fish will not survive.

A coastal freighter carrying feed from Vancouver offloads 1-tonne (1.1-ton) pallets of feed to a smaller vessel, which will deliver them to individual farm sites in Kyuquot Sound on Vancouver Island. A large salmon farm can go through up to 18 tonnes (19.8 tons) of feed per day.

PHOTO Peter A. Robson

INDUSTRIAL FISH AND FISHERIES

Most of the fish products used to manufacture feed come from wild fish caught off the coasts of Peru and Chile. The Coastal Alliance for Aquaculture Reform objects to this practice, saying that "underfed citizens in developing countries are deprived of a valuable source of protein in order to fulfill a luxury market in North America." Only small amounts of industrial or "feed grade" fish such as anchovy, jack mackerel, pilchard and capelin are in demand as food, because they are bony and contain little edible flesh (generally less than 30 percent of their body weight). Continuing efforts are being made by fishermen and processors to use more of these species for human food in order to add value to the catch, but those efforts have largely failed. The International Fishmeal and Fish Oil Organisation estimates that about 90 percent of the fish used to produce fishmeal and fish oil are not economically viable to process and are unmarketable in large quantities for human consumption.

Before large-scale aquaculture got underway and these fish were imported for processing into fishmeal and fish oil, they were used in the manufacture of fertilizers and industrial oils, used as lubricants and/or (depending on commodity markets) burned as fuel because they were cheaper than fossil-based products. Those uses have declined over the years as demand by the aquaculture sector rose, but fish oil was still being burned as fuel as recently as 2000. Fish oil was also used as a hardener in margarine and bakery products. Today, a small amount is used for human nutritional products such as fish-oil supplements.

Between 1984 and 2005, worldwide "capture" fisheries landed an average of 95 million tonnes (104.5 million tons) of fish of all types. Most of that was destined for direct human consumption. About 20–25 million tonnes (22–27.5 million tons) were used in the production of "industrial" or non-food products, including 6–7 million tonnes (6.5–7.5 million tons) of fishmeal and 1–1.7 million tonnes (1.1–1.9 million tons) of fish oil per year. About half the world supply of fishmeal is currently being used for aquaculture, primarily to raise salmon, trout and shrimp. The balance is used as a minor component in feed for land animals, including poultry, and in pet food. Of the fish oil produced, 80–90 percent is used by the aquaculture industry and a little more than half of that is used for salmon aquaculture.

Concerns have been raised that wild fish are being harvested at an unsustainable level by industrial fisheries. The United Nations Food and Agriculture Organization (FAO) keeps track of world capture fisheries and produces annual statistics. According to FAO, the world's catch of non-food fish has stayed at about 20–25 million tonnes (22–27.5 million tons) per year for the past several decades. This indicates that the ocean is producing new fish at the same rate as they are being caught, and therefore the stocks are likely sustainable at the current exploitation rate, which is quite feasible. Fish such as anchovy take only about a year to mature, so new fish are always being produced. As well, Chilean and Peruvian fisheries are strictly monitored. Stock in non-food fisheries is constantly being counted and controlled through individual vessel quotas, closed areas, seasonal bans, area and total catch limits, minimum net mesh sizes and satellite monitoring of fishboats. These countries also conduct their own research and work with international organizations that monitor fish stocks. The amount of fishmeal and fish oil produced globally is not determined by demand. It is set by governments to ensure that fishing is sustainable. Ironic as it may seem, this fishery may represent one of the few in the world being managed in what appears to be a truly sustainable way.

The capacity of the ocean to produce enough food for the many species in the food chain is affected by climatic changes. During El Niño weather events, warmer currents can disperse anchovy and other fish that live in the upper levels of the ocean, driving them deeper and/or away from their traditional feeding areas. As a result, catches can drop dramatically for a year or more and the effects can be felt throughout world production.

The FAO and the International Council for the Exploration of the Sea (ICES) monitor the status of fish stocks around the world. They report that the majority of fish stocks currently used to produce fishmeal and fish oil are within safe biological limits. One exception is blue whiting, a species caught in the North Atlantic and used in the European fishmeal industry. It is harvested in international waters by several countries, and stocks are currently being fished at an unsustainable level because the countries involved disagree on quotas.

Although the world supply of industrial fish has remained stable for many years, demand by the aquaculture sector has increased substantially. Between 1985 and 2000, production of farmed salmon grew from less than 50,000 tonnes to more than a million tonnes (55,000 to 1.1 million tons). The salmon aquaculture industry now uses about half of the world supply of fish oil and 15 percent of the fishmeal. China, which has recently entered the market for fishmeal and fish oil to supply both its poultry and its fast-growing fish-farming industry, uses more fishmeal and fish oil than any other country. As increasing demand has applied pressure to limited supply, the price of fishmeal and fish oil has risen steadily, and the aquaculture and meat-producing industries have reduced the proportion of fish-based products in their feeds by 20–50 percent and substituted cheaper plant-based products.

Concerns have been raised that the expanding aquaculture industry will press suppliers to overharvest and fish at unsustainable levels, or to exploit new species.

One solution for the aquaculture industry would be to use fish discarded by capture fisheries. A 2002 FAO report showed that some 25–30 million tonnes (27.5–33 million tons) of bycatch (also known as "trash" fish) from ocean fishing is being discarded annually— equal to the amount currently being supplied by the world's industrial fisheries.

In the end, though, manufacturers will most likely respond to increased demand for fishmeal and fish oil by reducing these ingredients in feeds and replacing them with something else.

NET LOSS OR NO LOSS

Every salmon we harvest—wild or farmed—represents a net loss of edible animal protein, because it takes more than a kilogram (2.2 lbs) of fish to produce a kilogram of growth in a salmon.

The aquaculture industry says that to raise farmed salmon is a significantly more efficient and sustainable use of aquatic resources than to harvest wild salmon. Fisheries biologists in both Canada and the U.S. have shown that a wild salmon typically needs to consume 5–15 kilograms (11–33 lbs) of forage fish to grow by 1 kilogram (2.2 lbs), because it must expend a lot of energy in searching out and capturing its prey. As well, for every wild salmon caught in the commercial fishery, at least one other must be allowed to spawn to replace the captured fish and sustain the population. That second fish also consumes 5–15 kg (11–33 lbs) of forage per kilogram of weight gain. Therefore, between 10 and 30 kg (22 to 66 lbs) of forage must be consumed to produce 1 kilogram (2.2 lbs) of table-ready wild salmon. To match the amount of fish produced in the B.C. salmon-farming industry in 2004 (61,800 tonnes/55,620 tons), wild salmon would have to consume 309,000–927,000 tonnes (278,100–834,300 tons) of wild forage, whereas the farmed salmon would consume only about 71,000 kilograms (78 tons) (see sidebar "How Many Wild Fish to Make a Farmed Fish?").

Assuming that farmed salmon use forage fish more efficiently than wild salmon, it is useful to question whether we would be better off eating the wild anchovy and mackerel, rather than converting them to feed and eating them as farmed salmon. The edible portion of such fish is about 30 percent of their body weight. In a salmon, the edible portion is about 65 percent, which means there is more meat per kilogram (2.2 lbs) on a salmon than on an anchovy or mackerel. If that anchovy or mackerel were converted to feed for salmon, that feed would produce over 50 percent more meat in the long run.

Where B.C.'s Fish Feed Comes From

The B.C. salmon-farming industry uses 25,000–30,000 tonnes (27,500–33,000 tons) of fishmeal and 15,000–20,000 tonnes (16,500–22,000 tons) of fish oil annually. About 10–15 percent of that comes from B.C. sources, such as reduction fisheries and offal. Most of the balance comes from Chile and Peru. B.C. uses less than 0.5 percent of the world production of fishmeal and 1.5 percent of the world production of fish oil.

Most of the feed used in B.C.'s salmon-farming industry is manufactured at one of two plants in the Lower Mainland: Cermaq (formerly EWOS), a Norwegian multinational company, and Skretting (formerly Moore-Clark Canada), owned by the Dutch multinational Nutreco Holdings N.V. Although some smaller feed producers operate in B.C., these two companies own feed plants around the world and together produce about 80 percent of the world supply of farmed-fish feed. They are vertically integrated companies that produce agricultural and aquaculture feed and own salmon farms around the world.

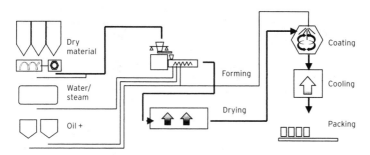

This simplified flow diagram shows how fish feed is manufactured. The ingredients are mixed together, extruded as pellets, dried, coated and then packed.

DIAGRAM courtesy Nutreco

FISHMEAL AND FISH OIL SUBSTITUTES

Feed is the single greatest expense for salmon farmers. It accounts for about half of the cost of raising fish. This, combined with the rising costs of fish oil and fishmeal, has fuelled a search for replacements for those key ingredients. Such replacements would also reduce any potential threat to sustainability of wild forage stocks.

One solution is to replace the fish-based proteins in feed with plant-based proteins. Greg Deacon, the nutritionist for the fish-feed manufacturer Skretting in Vancouver, says that Fisheries and Oceans Canada (DFO) and industry researchers in Vancouver are world leaders in developing the technology to replace fish products in feed. Researchers have experimented with different oils such as soy, canola and poultry, and fish-meal substitutes, such as mixtures of wheat gluten, corn gluten, canola meal, soybean meal, poultry meal and feather meal.

The major obstacle to using plant products is that fish cannot readily digest the complex carbohydrates found in plants and convert them into protein. Some compounds, such as those in canola meal and soybean meal, can be assimilated by fish, but others, such as fibre in the same plants, cannot—and they actually stop the "positive" elements from working. These are known as anti-nutritional compounds. Researchers are looking for ways to purify plant proteins by eliminating the "negative" elements.

Any new combinations have to meet the nutrient requirements of farmed salmon by providing the right combination of digestible amino acids, lipids and fatty acids. They must also be formulated to control fat levels, aroma and colour, and they must be stable enough that they do not turn rancid in storage. The more completely fish can assimilate the feed, the less feces go into the environment.

So far, Skretting has been able to replace all of the fishmeal in fish feed with canola concentrates with no loss of growth or change in feed conversion ratios (see sidebar "How Many Wild Fish to Make a Farmed Fish?") compared to normal diets, but not on a commercial scale. What the company has done over the last decade is to reduce the fish-meal content of their feeds by up to 70 percent and the fish-oil component by up to half. Today's feeds contain about 20 percent fish oil and 25 percent fishmeal.

How Many Wild Fish to Make a Farmed Fish?

To find out how many wild fish it takes to grow a farmed fish, John Kilpatrick and Greg Deacon of Skretting, a farmed-salmon feed manufacturer, did the math. The fish used in the manufacture of feed are rendered into both fish oil and fishmeal, and together represent about 45 percent of the content of fish feed. About 15 percent of the fish products used in fish feed consist of recycled fish trimmings (for example, fish heads and guts) from other commercial fisheries. Therefore, 15 percent has been deducted from the numbers of industrial fish in the calculation below.

(again, to trying the skew figures - guts & heads are still fish)

- ◆ An average of 1.2 kilograms (2.6 lbs) of feed is needed to produce 1 kilogram (2.2 lbs) of growth in a farmed salmon.
- ◆ That 1.2 kg of feed contains about 0.3 kg (0.66 lbs) of dried fishmeal (25 percent) and 0.24 kg (0.53 lbs) of fish oil (20 percent).
- ◆ 12 kg (26 lbs) of raw fish is needed to produce 1 kg (2.2 lbs) of fish oil. Therefore, based on the *oil* content of fish feed, 2.45 kg (5.4 lbs) of wild fish is needed to produce 0.24 kg (0.53 lbs) of fish oil.
- ◆ 4.5 kg (10 lbs) of raw fish is needed to produce 1 kg (2.2 lbs) of dried fishmeal. Therefore, based on the *fishmeal* content of fish feed, 1.14 kg (2.5 lbs) of wild fish is needed for 0.3 kg (0.66 lbs) of fishmeal.
- ◆ Using the higher number of fish required to produce the oil, it takes about 2.45 kg (5.4 lbs) of wild fish to produce 1 kg (2.2 lbs) of growth in farmed salmon.

In addition, Kilpatrick and Deacon point out that in obtaining oil from that 2.45 kg (5.4 lbs) of wild fish, 0.51 kg (1.1 lbs) of fishmeal is produced. As only 0.27 kg (0.59 lbs) of meal is required to grow 1 kg (2.2 lbs) of farmed salmon, 0.24 kg (0.53 lbs) is left over. That excess fishmeal is used to feed other animals, such as chickens (the poultry industry uses 24 percent of the world's fishmeal), so *+15%* it also produces 3.6 kg (8 lbs) of broiler chickens. Therefore, the amount of wild fish needed to produce 1 kg (2.2 lbs) of growth in a farmed salmon is 1.14 kg (2.5 lbs), whereas 5–15 kg (11–33 lbs) of wild forage is needed for every kilogram (2.2 lbs) of weight gain in a wild salmon.

OTHER INGREDIENTS IN FEED

Pigments

Carotenoids are a class of pigments that are synthesized in leaves, flowers, fruits and vegetables and give them their colour. Beta-carotene, the pigment that makes carrots orange, is the best-known carotenoid. Carotenoids are nutrients needed by all living organisms for proper growth, and they provide a number of other health benefits. They also give the flesh of wild salmon its red colour. Carotenoids cannot be synthesized by animals. Wild salmon get them by consuming tiny crustaceans such as krill and shrimp.

Because farmed salmon do not feed on crustaceans, they do not get carotenoids, and their flesh has a greyish tint. To make them more appealing to buyers and provide them with essential nutrients, salmon farmers add two carotenoids—astaxanthin and canthaxanthin—to the feed, singly or in combination. Astaxanthin occurs naturally in fish such as krill and shrimp, while canthaxanthin is predominant in many fruits, vegetables and flowers. Both pigments are available to salmon farmers in both natural and synthetic forms. They are costly and represent about 15 percent of the price of fish feed. These pigments are added to other common foods and drugs. Canthaxanthin, for example, is added to chicken feed to make egg yolks and poultry a brighter yellow.

In the same way that taking a vitamin C tablet provides the same amount of vitamin C as an orange, synthetic carotenoids are chemically identical to the natural compounds—they have the same

In addition to fishmeal, fish oil and vegetable-based products, feed contains pigments, antioxidants, vitamins and minerals. When ordered by a veterinarian, an antibiotic or chemical to control sea lice may also be added to the feed.

PHOTO courtesy B.C. Salmon Farmers Association

molecular structure. Carotenoids are supplied to farmed salmon in essentially the same concentration as they occur in wild salmon, 5–15 ppm (other than wild sockeye, 20–25 ppm). The only known detrimental health effect of these chemicals is associated with sunless tanning pills ingested orally by people. These pills contain canthaxanthin, and when overused they have caused retinal abnormalities. No health problems associated with synthetic canthaxanthin or astaxanthin have been observed in wild or farmed salmon, or any of the many other food products in which they are an ingredient. Their use has been approved in Canada by the Canadian Food Inspection Agency since 1990.

Antioxidants

Antioxidants are essential chemicals that remove potentially damaging oxidizing agents in living cells. Vitamins A, C and E are antioxidants, as are the carotenoids astaxanthin and canthaxanthin. Antioxidants are added to most manufactured foods as a preservative. In fish feed, they prevent oxidization of fats—feed would otherwise quickly turn rancid. Oxidization of fat can also make feed highly combustible. For this reason, government regulations require the addition of antioxidants to feed.

Nutritional Supplements

All living organisms contain most of the naturally occurring elements in the periodic table. Some 15 trace elements—chromium, cobalt, copper, iodine, iron, manganese, molybdenum, selenium, zinc and fluorine, among others—are known to be necessary for animals. Without them, fish would die. Vitamins are also essential to animal life. As farmed salmon don't get these vitamins and trace elements from their prey, they are added to the feed.

Genetically Modified Ingredients

To date, genetic modification—selecting specific genes from one organism and introducing them into another—has been used primarily in plants to make them more resistant to certain herbicides and pests. Over 25 percent of the world's farmland is planted with genetically modified (GM) crops. In North America, GM crops include corn, cotton, soybeans, canola and squash. In Canada, almost 5 million hectares (12.5 million acres) are planted with GM crops, most notably Roundup Ready canola.

GM plant products have been on the market for many years. In Canada and the U.S., most processed foods that contain soy, canola or corn contain some GM ingredients. Millions of tonnes of these products have been grown and consumed over the past decade with no apparent harm. But even if no food safety or human health issues arise with GM foods, there is concern about the longer-term effects and implications of "tinkering" with the evolutionary process, the natural environment and the disruption of traditional farming practices. In Europe, consumer resistance to GM products is strong, and Austria, France, Luxembourg, Germany, Italy, Greece and other countries have banned imports of these products, of which the U.S. is the primary producer.

The oil and meal from two genetically modified products, Roundup Ready canola and soybeans, are used as plant-based substitutes for fish ingredients in some fish feeds.

Rendered Animal Products
Fish and other animal-based proteins are much more digestible for carnivorous fish than plant-based proteins. Except for fish, poultry meal has proven to be the best and most economical source of protein for farmed salmon. Poultry meal is a dry product made from the non-food parts of poultry left over after processing. Feather meal is processed from the feathers. Because of the diet of poultry, these ingredients contain fewer PCBs and dioxins than marine ingredients. They are considered safe for use in salmon feed because there are no known pathogens that can be passed from warm-blooded poultry to cold-blooded salmon.

Hormones
Growth hormones, which are commonly given to beef and dairy cattle, are not used in B.C. in any farmed salmon destined for human consumption.

Medicated Feed

Medicine is added to feed only when disease occurs at a fish farm. The feed manufacturer gets a prescription order from a fish-health veterinarian and mixes the drug with the feed accordingly. The drugs used currently at B.C. salmon farms are four different antibiotics and one drug to treat sea lice.

Between 2 and 3 percent of the salmon feed produced in B.C. is medicated, compared to about 60 percent in beef and poultry feeds. About 90 percent of the antibiotics added to B.C. salmon-farm feed are used to treat chinook salmon—about 10 percent of the total farmed salmon—for bacterial kidney disease. The balance consists of antibiotics and the therapeutic lice treatment emamectin benzoate (SLICE) for use on both Pacific and Atlantic salmon. All medications used in feed are approved by Health Canada and administered under the supervision of a veterinarian.

In the early years of the industry, farm workers often handled drugs and mixed them into feed on site. Some workers developed health problems after being exposed to high doses of drugs. However, medicated feed is now premixed by the manufacturer under strictly controlled conditions and only upon veterinarian prescription. (For more on medications, see Chapter 6.)

So what happens
when the consumer eats
them?

SICKNESS AND HEALTH

Salmon Diseases and Treatments

When wild Pacific salmon return to their birth streams to spawn, it is naturally occurring disease that is typically responsible for their death.

PHOTO Peter A. Robson

PATHOGENS HAVE BEEN PRESENT IN THE AIR, SOIL AND WATER SINCE life first appeared on earth. In fact, bacteria are thought to be the organisms from which all life evolved. Pathogens are a natural part of any ecosystem and a function of life cycles. The pathogens that affect both wild and farmed salmon in British Columbia today have been around for many thousands of years, and humans cannot control them.

Exposure to pathogens does not necessarily cause a salmon to get sick, just as exposure to a flu virus does not mean that a human will become sick. The ability of a person (or fish) to resist disease after being exposed to a pathogen depends on a number of factors. The pathogen may not be concentrated enough, it may be unable to enter the host, it may be destroyed by natural immunity or it may not be virulent enough to cause illness. If the pathogen succeeds, it may make the person, or fish, temporarily ill or chronically ill, or it may prove fatal.

DYNAMICS OF PATHOGENS
Most pathogens get into the aquatic environment by being shed at some point by fish or other organisms that were carrying them.

First Contact
A pathogen can be transferred to a new host in three ways: via a vector—a third carrier that isn't affected by the pathogen—by physical contact or through exposure to a pathogen floating in the water column.

Vectors in the marine environment function in the same way as mosquitoes that transfer West Nile disease or malaria to humans. Little is known about vectors for salmon pathogens, though Fisheries and Oceans Canada (DFO) scientists are conducting research into the potential for sea lice to transfer pathogens among salmon. Meanwhile, vectors are not considered a significant factor in disease transfer among salmon.

Physical contact can also spread pathogens, though most contact among salmon occurs in their freshwater spawning grounds, where disease is rampant and where all salmon that make it back to their birth streams eventually succumb to predators or disease.

Some pathogens can survive in the water column, away from the host, long enough to make contact with new hosts. This depends on the type and nature of the pathogen, and the temperature and chemistry of the water. Survival time can range from a few hours to a few weeks. Tidal currents in the ocean and stream flows in fresh water both act as strong agents of dispersal. The farther a pathogen moves from its carrier and the more it is diluted, the less chance it has to lodge in a new host or to make the host sick. In bottom sediments, survival time can be much longer, but most pathogens that are buried in the sediment are unable to make contact with new hosts.

Once a fish comes into contact with a pathogen, it may or may not get sick, depending on the concentration, exposure period, strain and virulence of the pathogen. For a host to get enough of a dose to cause disease, the pathogen must be able to enter the host, establish itself and multiply. The host may have to have a wound, for example, or the pathogen may be able to enter the host via the exchange of salt water through its gills or organs.

Resistance

Should the pathogen become established and begin to multiply, the host's natural resistance and/or antibodies will attempt to eliminate the pathogen. Over millions of years, plants and animals have evolved together with the pathogens that affect them, and most species have developed some form of natural immunity or resistance.

This resistance works through two mechanisms: cellular immunity and antibody (or humoral) immunity. With cellular immunity, cells within a body's immune system detect, locate and attempt to kill infected cells when they are detected. With antibody immunity, when the body is first exposed to a pathogen, it produces a protein that targets that pathogen; and when exposed to the same pathogen again, the protein goes into action and stops it from gaining a foothold. This is how most vaccines work. The body is exposed to a small amount of the pathogen—typically dead, inactive or altered so it is non-pathogenic—and develops antibodies specific to that pathogen. When the body is exposed again, the antibodies can either destroy the pathogen, limit its ability to gain a foothold, or reduce or eliminate its effects.

Humans, salmon and other organisms may harbour many pathogens that their bodies can either coexist with, successfully fight off or eliminate—partly because of our natural immunity. As long as the host stays in good nutritional and physiological condition and lives in a healthy environment, its natural resistance protects it from many diseases.

The balance can be upset by a pathogen that is extremely virulent or one that a population has not previously been exposed to. Such a pathogen can overpower or avoid the natural defences of even a healthy host. For example, the 2004 outbreak of avian flu at poultry farms in southeastern B.C. was caused by a virulent pathogen that targeted poultry and overwhelmed even healthy birds.

Susceptibility

A fish or a population whose health is weakened for some reason is more susceptible, and this generally occurs because of a combination of factors.

Stress is a key factor. Fish, like humans, become more susceptible to sickness when they experience stress. They produce hormones that suppress their immune-system response—their ability to fight off pathogens—allowing otherwise relatively harmless diseases to take hold and spread infection.

Netpen salmon are stressed when they have to compete for food pellets every time they are fed, or when seals or other predators get into a netpen, or when staff handle fish to sort and transport them. Stress is also caused by social and territorial behaviour within the

Have you tried playing my Mozart for the Fish?

netpens, and changes in water quality, salinity and dissolved oxygen levels. Stress management and minimization is an extremely important aspect of successful salmon farming.

Wild salmon are stressed by many of the same factors: competition for feed, social interactions, predation and less than optimal environmental conditions. No studies have been done to measure and compare stresses on wild and farmed salmon. The only obvious difference is that wild salmon are better able to get away from predators, sick fish and areas with unfavourable environmental conditions.

DISEASE IN THE WILD

We know that about 98 percent of wild salmon do not survive to return and spawn, but little is known about the extent and frequency of disease epidemics in the wild. Because salmon spend much of their lives in the open ocean, it is almost impossible to monitor them.

Anyone who has seen carcasses of spawned-out salmon has witnessed the effects of naturally occurring diseases.

PHOTO Peter A. Robson

Disease epidemics do occur, and occasionally an epidemic is documented in nearshore waters when salmon return to their birth streams. Healthy salmon are known to carry certain pathogens for most of their lives without getting sick, but when they return to spawn, they are dying and their immune systems are suppressed. In several documented cases where large returns of weakened spawning salmon have been crowded and holding in warm, shallow waters at river mouths, diseases or parasite populations have exploded and caused extremely high mortalities.

Bacterial and viral disease epidemics are also observed

regularly in freshwater streams during the annual pink, chum and sockeye spawning events. These epidemics can devastate populations of juvenile salmon that are sharing the same waters and, months later, the offspring of the spawners. Other high-density natural events such as herring spawning can also serve to concentrate aquatic pathogens.

THE DISEASES DEFINED

The diseases that affect both wild and farmed salmon can be divided into four classes: fungal, bacterial, viral and parasitic. The viral, bacterial and fungal pathogens that affect farmed salmon have not been shown to affect humans who consume fish that are or were sick. The only exceptions are those caused by poor handling and preparation, which can affect all types of wild and farmed seafood. (For more on parasites, see Chapter 7. For more on consumption of farmed salmon, see Chapter 10.)

FUNGAL DISEASES

Fungus spores occur naturally in rivers and streams, and fungal diseases usually affect salmon in the freshwater, or hatchery, stage of their lives. No significant fungal diseases affect farmed salmon in salt water.

Whether a hatchery is raising eggs to enhance wild stocks or to produce farmed fish, when fungus spores find their way into a hatchery they can attach to incubating eggs or fry, reproduce and overwhelm their host. Salmon eggs are particularly susceptible to fungal infection because of their high density in incubation trays. Dead eggs, of which there are a few in every batch, are easy hosts for fungal spores. Once a fungal infection gets established on eggs, it forms a cloudy mat and can suffocate live eggs.

Hatchery operators attempt to prevent fungus by using ground (well) water, where fungus doesn't normally occur, or by filtering and/or sterilizing their surface (creek) water supplies. As well, salmon eggs are typically surface-disinfected with a formaldehyde or iodine-based antifungal agent before they are placed in incubation trays. They are treated again whenever they are handled.

BACTERIAL DISEASES

Bacteria are ever-present in the environment and essential to life. In the bodies of most higher life forms, including humans, many surface and internal bacterial communities are active. Food could not be digested without bacteria. In healthy animals, the "good" bacteria keep the "bad" (pathogenic) bacteria in check. However, when given the chance, pathogenic bacteria can overwhelm the good bacteria and cause disease. Some of the world's most deadly disease outbreaks—typhoid, cholera, plague, tuberculosis, botulism—have been caused by pathogenic bacteria.

Bacteria cause disease by attaching themselves to a body or by invading cells, producing toxins and multiplying. In salmon, they are transmitted through the feces and mucus of infected fish as well as through decaying dead fish. Although some bacteria are opportunistic and can survive in the environment without a host, most cannot. Some last only a few hours without a host; no bacteria can last longer than a few weeks.

A number of bacteria can cause disease in fish and some are more problematic in certain species and regions than in others. The bacterial ailments of most concern to salmon farming are bacterial kidney disease, furunculosis, vibriosis and enteric redmouth disease, all of which can cause serious and recurring losses in pen-reared salmon.

Bacterial Kidney Disease (BKD)

The bacteria *Renibacterium salmoninarum* causes BKD. It is naturally occurring and widespread in wild Pacific salmon. For farms raising chinook and coho, BKD is a significant cause of mortality. Atlantics are also susceptible, but losses are primarily of small fish, whereas in Pacific salmon, more chronic losses occur in larger fish at or near harvest size.

The BKD pathogen is transmitted in two ways: from parent to offspring through eggs (vertically), as well as through contact in fresh and salt water (horizontally). An outbreak of BKD can occur at any point during the life cycle of salmon and at any time of year.

BKD causes severe chronic inflammation of the kidney and, to a lesser degree, the tissues of other organs and muscle. Once it takes hold, BKD develops slowly into a persistent condition and can become fatal. Fish affected by BKD are described as lethargic, dark-coloured and partially blind, and they often have skin abscesses that can break open. The BKD bacteria is so prevalent among wild fish that fish-health experts say the risk of their being infected by farm sources is very low. Enhancement hatcheries report that up to 50 percent of returning coho collected for broodstock are infected, even though all the eggs used to produce them were screened for BKD and all infected eggs were destroyed. To prevent BKD, farmed broodstock are given antibiotics before being spawned. As well, samples from every female are sent for screening and if BKD is discovered, all of that female's eggs are discarded. A vaccine, Renogen, is currently being used to limit BKD, although researchers have found it difficult to vaccinate against BKD. Renogen stimulates the immune system to produce antibodies that will react with BKD, but BKD can be present in the cells of both tissue and eggs, where it is not always recognized by the immune system.

Furunculosis
Furunculosis, which induces severe hemorrhaging of the internal organs, is caused by the *Aeromonas salmonicida* bacteria. It occurs in the Pacific and Atlantic oceans and is generally only found in fresh water. Outbreaks have been seen in the wild during spawning, when fish are stressed due to high densities, high water temperatures, low water flow and aggressive interactions over spawning territory—conditions that are ideal for its spread. Furunculosis can also be passed from spawning adults to juvenile fish sharing the same river. It is not transmitted vertically (from parent to offspring), and it can be eliminated by surface disinfection of eggs.

The pathogen can be carried in the water column and infect salmon farms many kilometres apart. It is thought to be able to remain active in salt water, in the absence of a host, from four to eight days.

Furunculosis is rarely found in farmed Pacific salmon in salt water. Between 2003 and mid-2005, no furunculosis was found in either hatcheries or farms raising Pacific salmon. Atlantic salmon are more susceptible to it. When it does occur, it is most often the result of infected stream water flowing into a hatchery. Furunculosis is considered self-limiting because should a smolt carrying the bacteria be transferred to salt water, it will either die or no longer be affected by furunculosis.

Furunculosis outbreaks have been greatly reduced in Atlantic salmon in recent years thanks to the development of a highly effective vaccine. When the vaccine does not work, antibiotics have proven effective.

Vibriosis (Listonella)

A number of naturally occurring *Vibrio* species affect saltwater fish and invertebrates around the world. Two of them, *Vibrio anguillarum* and *Vibrio ordalli*, affect salmon farms. In both wild and farmed Pacific and Atlantic salmon, fish that have vibriosis show internal hemorrhaging, systemic (methodical) infections and, in severe cases, deep red ulcers on the skin. Because these bacteria are a normal part of the aquatic environment, wild fish are constantly exposed to them, but they are more opportunistic than most pathogens and generally affect only the most susceptible fish. Vibrios are thought to be able to remain active in salt water for more than a year.

Vibriosis has been almost completely eliminated at salmon farms in recent years, thanks to the development of an effective vaccination against the disease. According to the Fish Health Database, between 2003 and mid-2005, vibriosis was reported in only two fish groups.

Enteric Redmouth Disease

Enteric redmouth disease (ERM) is caused by the bacterial pathogen *Yersinia ruckeri*. It is known primarily for its occurrence in rainbow trout. ERM was first identified in Idaho in the 1950s and has since been recorded in most trout-producing regions of the world. Scientists once speculated that it spread from Idaho through the transportation of infected carriers. However, different strains are found in different geographic areas, and ERM is now thought to be a naturally occurring pathogen, though the culturing of trout may have made it abundant.

The bacteria affects both wild and farmed Pacific salmon as well as farmed Atlantic salmon. It occurs primarily in fresh water, and fry are the most susceptible. ERM most often results in sustained low-level mortality, but it can result in high losses, usually when chronically ill fish are weakened further by stressors such as transportation or poor environmental conditions. Outbreaks are most often associated with significant changes in water temperature. Once a host is infected, higher water temperatures allow the bacteria to multiply rapidly. Chronically affected fish are typically lethargic and swim near the surface. If the disease progresses, it can cause hemorrhages of the mouth and gills—hence the "redmouth" in the name.

The pathogen spreads from fish to fish by contact with infected fish or carriers. It is not known to be transmitted from parent to offspring. The spread of the bacteria has been prevented by the surface disinfection of eggs, the use of sterilized or filtered well and/or creek water, vaccination and good husbandry. When an outbreak occurs, an antibiotic medicated feed may be prescribed by the attending veterinarian.

Because the pathogen comes from wild fish—whether carriers or infected individuals—and because Pacific salmon have a built-in immunity, ERM is not thought to be a threat to wild fish. The Fish Health Database reported four occurrences of ERM among Atlantic salmon in fresh water between 2003 and mid-2005, and three among Atlantic salmon in salt water.

Treatments for Bacterial Disease

For any disease, prevention is always preferable to illness and treatment. One of the most important methods of prevention is to vaccinate juvenile fish against the most common bacterial diseases before the fish are transferred to saltwater netpens. This protects not only individual fish but the whole population. Today, almost all farmed salmon are vaccinated, either by direct injection or topically in a bath treatment (though the latter is less effective). Good husbandry practices such as managing fish to reduce stress have also contributed significantly to the prevention of bacterial disease at salmon farms.

Vaccines are never 100 percent effective. Under certain conditions—when fish are weakened for some reason, or when strong pathogens are present—vaccines can be overwhelmed and the fish can be unable to fight off infection. When an outbreak occurs at a salmon farm, the fish may be treated with a specially formulated feed containing an antibiotic prescribed by the attending veterinarian and mixed into the feed by the manufacturer. Or the outbreak can be resolved simply by changing the husbandry practices.

Most common bacterial outbreaks that require antibiotics can be cleared up with a 10-day treatment, but for BKD, the treatment can be as long as 21 days. Treatment also varies according to the water temperature, which affects the appetite of fish.

When a bacterial disease occurs, the entire population of the farm is treated, even if only a small percentage of the fish are sick. This approach reduces the proportion of individuals who become infected, the number of infected individuals who show signs of sickness and the number who become seriously ill or die.

Four approved antibiotics are licensed for use under veterinarian prescription at salmon farms. They are Terramycin Aqua (oxytetracycline), Aquaflor (florfenicol), Tribrissen 40 (sulfadiazine/trimethoprim) and Romet 30 (sulfadimethoxine/ormetoprim).

Oxytetracycline makes up close to 90 percent of the antibiotics used in B.C. Of that amount, about 90 percent is used to treat BKD in coho and chinook, even though Pacific salmon make up less than 15 percent of B.C.'s farmed salmon production. A large dose is required to treat BKD (100 milligrams per kilogram/0.002 oz per lb) and farmed chinook need regular treatment. In contrast, the dose of Aquaflor required to treat an outbreak of furunculosis is 10 mg/kg (0.0003 oz/lb). Oxytetracycline is mixed into feed at a ratio of 16–45 kg/tonne (32–91 lbs/ton), and 44 percent of that is the active ingredient.

Several chinook growers in the industry have combined rigorous screening and a high level of stress management and vaccination to produce market chinook without using antibiotics.

In general, the cost of vaccination is more than offset by higher survival and more rapid growth in salmon. This is reflected in the fact that only about 2 to 3 percent of all feed used at salmon farms in B.C. is medicated—and this includes non-antibiotic drugs such as those used to treat sea lice.

Antibiotics and the Environment

Only about 2 percent of the farmed salmon raised in B.C. in any given year are treated with antibiotics, so they account for only a fraction of the medical antibiotic residues that end up in our waters through human sewage. When these fish are being treated for bacterial disease through the necessary 10- to 21-day period, antibiotics can leach into the environment through fish and uneaten feed.

In the early years of salmon farming, the fish simply didn't like medicated feed. Today, feed containing oxytetracycline is no more or less palatable than regular feed, though sick fish eat less than healthy ones. Because the feeding operations at most salmon farms in B.C. are monitored by underwater cameras (to conserve feed), feeding ceases as soon as the fish stop eating. Therefore, the amount of feed that falls through the net (about 4 percent) is likely the same whether or not the fish are sick.

Once consumed, the antibiotics are absorbed into the fish's bloodstream, where they go to work to kill the targeted bacteria. A portion of the antibiotics is later secreted through the gills, urine and feces. A study by Aquametrix Research found that it takes about a week for traces of the antibiotic to show up in the water column and/or sediments.

When oxytetracycline is excreted from fish, any active ingredients bind to the calcium and magnesium ions that occur naturally in salt water, and become inert. The study found that although traces of the drug can remain close to a salmon farm using antibiotics, the drug is inert and has no effect on any living organisms. These residues break down naturally over time and eventually disappear, a process that can take days or weeks depending on local environmental conditions such as water temperature and salinity.

Some of the 4 percent of the feed that falls through the netcage is eaten by other species. But because neither feed nor antibiotics are toxic, even if the antibiotics had not yet become inert, the ingestion of the small amount of antibiotics has never been shown to harm aquatic life.

The rest of the feed settles among the bottom sediments. Although the active ingredients in the antibiotics remain active for a few days or a few weeks, studies by scientists in B.C. and Washington State have shown that these small amounts of antibiotics do not reduce the natural microbial populations or activity that takes place under salmon farms.

Because a very small percentage of people are allergic to antibiotics, provincial regulations prohibit the harvest of any farmed salmon that contains potentially harmful antibiotic residues. A mandatory withdrawal period must be allowed before the fish are harvested. The Canadian Food Inspection Agency is responsible for monitoring food safety and spot-auditing fish products for the presence of drug residues. Residues of antibiotics in the flesh of any fish destined for human consumption may not exceed established Health Canada maximums.

Resistance to Antibiotics

Sometimes bacteria become resistant to a specific drug that is used to control them, and this antibiotic drug becomes ineffective in treating the disease. Antibiotic resistance is now considered to be one of the most serious risks to human health in the world. According to CBS News, in North America alone, over 130 million prescriptions for antibiotics are written every year and about half of those are written unnecessarily, for viruses and other ailments that are not affected by antibiotics. The misuse and overuse of antibiotics is the primary reason that bacteria develop resistance.

Between 10 and 40 percent of any bacterial strain is naturally resistant. This is a built-in survival mechanism: these are the bacteria that survive when antibiotics are used repeatedly or at levels that are too low to be effective. When they reproduce—which they can only do on a host—the next generation is more resistant, and so on until they are completely resistant to the antibiotic. As long as the host is alive and the antibiotic is being used, the process of selection pressure will continue and the resistant bacteria will dominate.

In most cases, the "new" resistant strain is not viable on its own, and the antibiotic remains effective only until a viable variant emerges. Should a new strain emerge, it may or not be more virulent than the original. Most bacteria have developed over thousands of years and have changed very little because there was no reason to change.

Should a bacteria develop resistance to a specific antibiotic, that resistance is not permanent. Once selection pressure stops—when a drug is no longer administered—those bacteria are no longer forced to select that resistance, and the resistant characteristic recedes. Other "normal" bacteria from the environment enter the population. The natural population makeup is restored within about five or six months, depending on the species and the bacteria, and once again the drug is effective.

At salmon farms, almost all antibiotic treatments are administered for less than three weeks, so there is little concern among veterinarians that resistance will develop. In an unpublished Health Canada study of the risks of transfer of resistance, researchers found very low levels of resistance among fish pathogens. Provincial government veterinarians constantly monitor bacterial pathogens in farmed fish and say that they are simply not finding resistance. They are much more concerned about resistance in land-based agriculture, where some poultry and swine are fed antibiotics as a preventative measure for their entire lives.

In these times of headlines warning of avian flu and antibiotic-resistant "superbugs," it is natural to wonder whether a resistant strain of bacteria could be transferred to humans. Such a transfer is highly unlikely, because humans and fish have completely different sets of pathogens. Farmed fish do not carry human bacteria such as E. coli or salmonella (no relation to salmon). Most salmon pathogens do not grow at human body temperature ($37°C/98.6°F$) and therefore do not thrive or even survive in humans. Health Canada has found no salmon pathogens that might raise significant human health concern. The same cannot be said of land-based animal farming, because the pathogens of warm-blooded humans and animals can overlap.

In the early years of salmon farming in B.C., before the development of a variety of antibiotics for use at farms and the widespread use of effective vaccines, antibiotic-resistant strains of furunculosis bacteria did develop at farm sites. In 1993, the year of the first occurrence, only one antibiotic (oxytetracycline) was available to treat furunculosis. Because of poor management processes, the drug was overused and the bacteria in those fish became resistant. However, resistance is developed only in the host, so once those fish were harvested, the bacteria were removed from the environment. In the few other instances when bacteria have become resistant, the situation was also temporary. If resistance were a growing problem at salmon farms, more antibiotics would have to be used. In fact, according to statistics and provincial veterinarians, antibiotic use has remained stable over the last decade. Veterinarians report improvements in vaccines and management practices—such as more efficient disease detection, diagnosis and treatment. These changes have resulted in healthier, less susceptible fish.

VIRUSES

Viruses can be found in humans, animals, plants and even within bacteria. Even normal sea water has been shown to contain great numbers of viral pathogens. Most humans harbour some forms of virus, though most of the time we don't get sick. Other viruses are responsible for such diseases as chicken pox, herpes, measles, colds and flu.

Viruses work by invading host cells, replicating themselves within the host cells, replicating the host cells and spreading to other tissue via the bloodstream or nervous system. When the body's immune system detects a virus, it attempts to eliminate it by producing antibodies or otherwise impairing its ability to reproduce. In some cases, the virus causes the body to kill its own cells as a defence mechanism. Drugs—including antibiotics—are mostly ineffective in killing viruses. Most treatments, such as cold medicines, can only relieve the symptoms caused by the virus. The most effective control measure for viruses is vaccination. No highly effective vaccinations for salmon-related viruses are available, though several are in the experimental stages.

The viruses known to affect salmon in the aquatic environment occur naturally. Through evolution, Pacific salmon have developed some natural immunity to the viral pathogens common in the Pacific basin. Viruses that affect salmon can exist in the wild, but they cannot reproduce outside living cells. Most viruses affect farmed salmon infrequently and have only a minor impact on stocks.

Infectious Hematopoeitic Necrosis (IHN)

Only one viral disease is of significant concern to salmon farmers in B.C.: infectious hematopoietic necrosis (IHN), also known as sockeye disease or sockeye flu. The virus was first recognized in the 1950s. Like all viruses that affect farmed salmon, it occurs naturally in B.C.'s wild salmon. It works by selectively attacking the organs that support the immune system, thereby compromising the fish's ability to fight illness. The virus is very infectious, spreads rapidly between fish and can kill large numbers in a population. IHN has been found in wild sockeye, chinook, coho and rainbow trout, as well as a variety of non-salmonid fish, including herring.

Most outbreaks in the wild occur among sockeye that are spawning in fresh water, where it is common. The virus takes hold when the immune systems of sockeye carriers are weakened by impending death and by stress factors such as crowding on the spawning beds, high water temperatures and low stream flows. Infected sockeye die in their spawning streams and shed the virus into the water, transmitting it to other fish—typically juvenile salmon sharing the same stream. The virus can also be spread by infected female sockeye (those that survive long enough to spawn) to their eggs. Once a fish gets the virus, it usually becomes infected and dies within 5 or 10 days. However, some juvenile fish survive the infection and become carriers when they leave their spawning streams and migrate to salt water. Resistant wild fish may carry the disease, but DFO researchers believe outbreaks in the saltwater environment are uncommon. Sockeye, however, have been known to begin developing physical signs of the IHN virus on their homeward migration.

IHN is of great concern to fish farmers because it is extremely virulent to Atlantic salmon, which probably lack natural immunity to it, and there is no way to treat an outbreak when it occurs. The result is often extensive losses to a farmed salmon population. Farmed chinook, however, are not affected.

Outbreaks of IHN in Atlantic salmon at B.C. fish farms were first reported in 1992. Inmigrating adult sockeye and other species, such as herring—known to be IHN carriers—are thought by DFO researchers to be travelling reservoirs of IHN and to be spreading the pathogen to farmed Atlantic salmon. The virus appears in various

IHN Outbreaks in B.C.

The first confirmed outbreak of IHN in salmon farms in B.C. took place from 1992 to 1996 and affected 13 farms in the Campbell River/Quadra Island area. A second outbreak occurred from 2001 to 2003 and affected 36 farms, many of them near Vancouver Island. The second occurrence was brought under control much faster than the original outbreak—23 months compared to 42 months. No IHN outbreaks were reported in 2004 or 2005.

The most controversial handling of an IHN outbreak occurred in February 2002, when 1.6 million infected Atlantic salmon smolts from a Heritage Salmon site in the Broughton archipelago were to be disposed of by being rendered into fishmeal at the Bella Coola Fisheries plant on the Fraser River. First Nations and environmental groups obtained a court injunction and stopped the plan, saying that the water in the holds of the fish packer could spread IHN and threaten wild fish in the Fraser River, the largest salmon-producing river in the world. Heritage Salmon had already arranged to have the waste water disinfected under the supervision of a veterinarian, and the process had been approved by DFO. The injunction was subsequently lifted, but meanwhile the fish were taken to Courtenay, B.C., where they were composted into fertilizer (the heat from decomposition kills the virus), and the waste water was disinfected according to the previous plan.

At the time the injunction was ordered, millions of wild IHN-carrying sockeye had been processed at plants along the Fraser River for over 100 years and the blood water had been discharged directly back into the Fraser River. No plans were in place to change this practice.

---

geographic regions of the coast in a yet-undefined pattern. Some years it causes massive losses to salmon farmers; other years it doesn't appear at all. DFO researchers speculate that this is the result of the virus being more widespread in certain year classes of sockeye. Perhaps specific genetic pools carry higher levels and they are most likely to pass the virus on to farmed fish.

To keep IHN to a minimum, salmon farmers screen all female broodstock and all smolts before they are transferred from fresh water to their saltwater netpens. Many Atlantic salmon are now being vaccinated as well, though the IHN vaccines currently in use are effective only at low levels. Salmon farmers also try to reduce stress on the fish being raised in netpens.

Because the virus comes from outside the netpens and salmon farmers cannot control the movement of wild fish, they cannot predict where or when it will strike. Some operations have significantly reduced IHN losses by using existing vaccines, effective stress management and good biosecurity.

When an outbreak occurs, mortality varies between fish of different ages, but mortality rates are usually highest in netpens containing Atlantic smolts. Sometimes a farm containing a million fish loses only a few smolts; in other cases, 75 percent of a population is killed in a three-week to three-month period.

Younger fish are more vulnerable to disease in general. When IHN occurs in a pen containing smolts that have been at sea for less than six months, it is often more economical to slaughter the entire population and start over than to wait for the infection to run its course. IHN tends to have less impact on older, larger fish (2–3 kilograms/4½–6½ lbs). Some clinical infection may occur, but enough healthy fish usually remain that they reach market size and can be harvested over a period of several months. As with other diseases of wild and farmed salmon, there are no health risks for humans who eat fish that carry the IHN virus. Most wild sockeye carry the virus and they are approved for consumption.

The salmon farmer's decision is more difficult when the fish have spent a year in salt water and weigh 1–2 kilograms (2.2–4.5 lbs). At this point, they are still more than 100 days away from the minimum market size of 3 kg (6.5 lbs). They are too small to harvest and sell, yet the salmon farmer has incurred substantial costs in raising them to this point. Among this age class, the virus can kill as many as 40 percent of the fish, but the salmon farmer may be reluctant to slaughter all the fish in the infected pen simply as a precautionary measure. The IHN pathogen is indigenous, so there are no regulations requiring the slaughter of infected fish. As well, a salmon farmer's insurance may cover fish that die from disease or outside causes such as algal blooms, but it won't compensate for fish killed just to be on the safe side.

The IHN virus can survive from several days to several weeks without a host in salt water, so it can spread from one infected farm to another aboard fish carriers, or through the movement of personnel or boats, and/or through the transportation of live fish past infected sites.

To limit the spread of the virus during an outbreak, strict biosecurity measures are implemented. The movement of all personnel, equipment and boats is controlled: for example, separate mort dive teams operate at each site. Special procedures are implemented for the removal and disposal of dead fish. When harvested, the blood water is disinfected or pumped to treatment facilities ashore.

When the last of the live fish—the ones that have remained healthy—are harvested, the site is emptied, disinfected, then fallowed for several months or until the salmon farmer is sure the virus has been eliminated. However, because the pathogen is carried by wild fish, the farm may become infected again at any time.

When salmon infected with IHN continue to live in their netpens, they continuously shed the virus into the aquatic environment. Like all pathogens, the IHN virus can potentially be transmitted to susceptible wild fish. However, provincial government health officials consider the risks to be minimal, because the virus is already carried by many wild species, which appear to have some form of natural immunity and do not get sick. In 2005 a new IHN vaccine for Atlantic salmon was approved for use in B.C. However, it will take several years for its effectiveness to be evaluated properly.

IMPACT OF DISEASE
SUSCEPTIBILITY OF WILD AND FARMED SALMON

The same pathogens affect wild and farmed salmon, but they do not affect all fish in the same way, and farmed salmon may be more or less susceptible to a pathogen than wild Pacific salmon.

Some 15 million years ago, Atlantic salmon were widespread throughout the northern hemisphere. Pacific salmon eventually dominated and Atlantics became extinct in the Pacific basin millions of years ago. As well, Pacific salmon have never lived in the Atlantic basin. Therefore, Atlantic salmon don't have much history of coexisting with pathogens indigenous to the Pacific Ocean and are therefore more susceptible to such organisms as the IHN virus. These pathogens can be carried and passed on by Pacific salmon, which are less affected by them.

Over many millennia, Pacific salmon have learned to make one-way spawning migrations, then die on the spawning beds in large numbers. In their final days, as they weaken before dying, they typically become riddled with disease and shed enormous numbers of pathogens into the water. To avoid annihilation, Pacific salmon have therefore evolved a necessary resistance to indigenous pathogens such as bacterial kidney disease (BKD), furunculosis and viruses.

Atlantic salmon can spawn over several years, so they have not had to confront the pathogen loads associated with dying Pacific salmon and to build up the same level of resistance. For example, in farmed Atlantic salmon, BKD—the most common pathogen in Pacific salmon—causes the highest mortalities in smolts and younger fish, but in Pacific salmon it is usually more chronic and can kill more adult fish. Even within Pacific salmon populations, susceptibility varies with species. Wild coho and chinook salmon are known to be carriers of the IHN virus, but the pathogen apparently affects only sockeye and chum salmon in fresh water.

MUTATION OF PATHOGENS

All the pathogens that affect farmed salmon in B.C. are indigenous. Viruses, bacteria and parasites have evolved alongside the species they affect for tens of thousands of years. During that time, pathogens and their hosts have developed a natural balance. If the pathogen were too virulent, it would kill too many individuals and die for lack of a host. If it were too weak, it would not be able to reproduce in numbers to sustain itself and it would also die. Once this balance is reached, there is not normally any pressure for a pathogen to change.

When genetic change does occur, it is usually in response to external factors such as a change in hosts or in the environment. That is why antibiotics that are used to treat disease outbreaks can force a pathogen to change: the pathogen must select those parts of its makeup that can survive the new conditions. That feature will then be produced in greater quantities by each subsequent generation until a balance is reached with the new conditions. Such changes occur very slowly, and the success rate of new strains is very low, because new strains tend to be weaker and to dissipate over time unless they are under constant pressure. As well, when a new strain does survive, it is not always more virulent than the original. When the selection pressure is removed, mutant or resistant strains have no particular advantage, and the overall mix of genotypes will tend to revert to the original state.

If a salmon farm did cause change in the makeup of a pathogen, once that fish population was harvested, the new pathogen's host would be removed and the original strain that is always present in the environment would be restored.

No drug treatment is available to cure indigenous viruses in B.C., so there is no pressure to adapt. Some viruses do tend to change more than others. The flu virus in humans, for example, is constantly changing. In B.C., the genetic makeup of the IHN virus is monitored for change. It has been shown to change very slightly from strain to strain, but it has not become any more or less virulent, and clinically (the way it manifests itself) it has remained exactly the same.

Vaccines for bacterial diseases can also force new strains to develop. No vaccine is 100 percent effective. When disease does occur after vaccination, it is usually because some fish-management problem has made the fish more susceptible, allowing the pathogen to overwhelm the vaccine and the fish's natural immunity. If fish were becoming diseased because of vaccine-resistant pathogens, more disease outbreaks would occur in B.C. and more fish would die as a result. According to the Ministry of Agriculture and Lands, disease is not on the rise.

Fresh Silvers

In the fall of 2002, the B.C. Salmon Farmers Association and Ministry of Agriculture and Lands (MAL) created the Fish Health Database, which requires salmon farmers to provide data on all fish-health events that required veterinarian intervention. This information is audited by MAL inspectors and the results are posted quarterly on the ministry's Fish Health website.

Among the data posted is the number of mortalities that occur at salmon farms and the cause of the mortalities. The numbers show that the average mortality from disease or suspected disease (classed as "fresh silvers") in 2003 averaged almost 5 percent for Pacific salmon and 9 percent for Atlantic salmon. In 2004, the annual mortality was 2.7 percent among Pacific salmon and

1 percent among Atlantic salmon. In the first half of 2005, mortality from disease was about 1 percent among Pacific salmon and about 0.6 percent among Atlantic salmon. Mortalities for Atlantic salmon were higher than average in 2003 because of IHN virus outbreaks at many farms. These figures are provided by salmon farmers, but provincial fish health inspectors say they visit about 30 percent of salmon farms each year to monitor fish health.

EXOTIC PATHOGENS

The introduction of an exotic pathogen to B.C. waters could have devastating consequences. The immunity that B.C.'s wild fish have developed to local pathogens would not protect them from an unfamiliar pathogen.

To enhance sport fishing in the early years of the 20th century, millions and millions of Atlantic salmon eggs, alevins, fry and smolts were intentionally introduced to 60 different lakes, rivers and streams in B.C. Fortunately, no new pathogens are known to have been introduced as a result, and Atlantic salmon did not become established.

When the salmon-farming industry realized there were significant advantages to raising Atlantic salmon over Pacific salmon, scientists and other citizens raised concerns that exotic pathogens and parasites would inevitably hitchhike along and spread to wild fish. The import of Atlantic salmon eggs was allowed anyway, but before the first eggs were imported for salmon farming in 1985, the federal government introduced the Canadian Fish Health Protection Regulations, which oversaw the movement of Atlantic salmon eggs into Canada and across provincial boundaries. The regulations specified quarantine measures for eggs and the disinfection of eggs and effluent. Surface disinfection of eggs is only 99.98 percent effective, so the regulations also require monthly testing of quarantined juvenile fish for pathogens, for at least one full year after they hatch, to ensure they are disease-free before being moved to saltwater grow-out pens.

135

A Sampler of Exotic Diseases

Salmon farming is not known to have introduced any new pathogens into our waters, but exotic pathogens have been introduced accidentally in B.C. and around the world and resulted in significant problems when exposed to stocks that have a reduced ability to resist them.

The **Gyrodactylus salaris** parasite was discovered in freshwater streams in Norway after trout carrying the parasite were introduced from Sweden to enhance local populations. The trout were raised in Norwegian hatcheries that were also raising Atlantic juveniles. The parasite spread between species, and once those hatchery fish were released, they spread the disease to wild fish. To control the spread and impact of the parasite, the Norwegian government deliberately poisoned 24 rivers with the pesticide Rotenone, which also killed all other life in the rivers. The parasite still has not been exterminated and has recolonized several of the Rotenone-treated rivers. Norwegian salmon farmers sued the Norwegian government and were awarded damages. *Gyrodactylus salaris* is a freshwater parasite that is not known to affect netcage salmon, and the incident in Norway had nothing to do with farmed salmon.

Whirling disease, caused by the *Myxobolus cerebralis* parasite, is native to European salmonids. It is a freshwater parasite that was inadvertently introduced to the eastern United States in 1955 in shipments of trout. The parasite somehow found its way into fresh water and has since spread to 22 U.S. states and caused significant losses in wild rainbow trout populations and in trout hatcheries. Although it is harmless to humans and other wildlife, the parasite causes deformity in its host, which makes the host "whirl" in a tail-chasing pattern. The parasite eventually causes death in some species of trout, but wild and farmed salmon have not been affected. *Myxobolus cerebralis* is unusual in the way it spreads. Infected fish shed spores into the water column, but the spores are not infective until they pass through the digestive tract of an intermediate host, the tubifex worm. These worms are found in fresh water throughout North America. Fish can also be infected by eating worms containing spores of the pathogen. Where it occurs, whirling disease can be controlled by raising trout in tanks instead of earthen ponds. Because Canada only allows the import of surface-disinfected eggs, not live fish, for aquaculture, and because the parasites do not live inside eggs, this parasite is unlikely to be introduced as a result of salmon farming.

When the **infectious salmon anemia (ISA)** virus was reported on the east coast of Canada, it was thought to have been imported from Europe. The virus was first identified at Norwegian salmon farms in 1984. It may have been indigenous to Norway before salmon farming began, but was not detected. Between 1984 and 1990, it caused significant losses at almost 100 Norwegian salmon farms. A variant appeared in Chile in 1999 and in the Faeroe Islands in 2000, and ISA has since been found in wild salmon, trout and eels in Scotland. The virus appeared in New Brunswick salmon farms in 1996, and then in Nova Scotia. Between 1998 and June 2000, 55 New Brunswick farms were infected. The government ordered millions of fish killed and it quarantined the affected farms. The virus was later detected in wild Atlantic salmon in a river in New Brunswick. In 1998 it was detected in Nova Scotia, and in 2001 it appeared in Maine, where millions of Atlantic salmon had to be killed. All the netpens in Cobscook Bay were emptied of fish, cleaned and disinfected in an attempt to stop the spread of the virus. The ISA virus was first thought to have been imported to North America in Atlantic salmon eggs, but scientists found that the New Brunswick strain is genetically different from the European strains—it is indigenous to the Canadian Atlantic provinces and wherever else it occurs. All introductions of Atlantic salmon eggs for aquaculture in B.C. have been carried out under strict quarantine and supervision of DFO fish-health personnel. ISA has not been introduced to B.C., and for the past 10 years no Atlantic salmon eggs have been brought in from Europe or any other place where ISA is prevalent.

MONITORING FOR DISEASE

At harvest, a salmon farm can contain up to 900,000 adult salmon worth approximately $13.5 million. Therefore, as with farmers of land-based animals, it is in the financial interest of salmon farmers to take every measure to raise healthy fish by vaccinating their stock and observing good husbandry practices.

To this end, at both hatcheries and netpen sites, staff constantly monitor the feeding patterns and other behaviour of the salmon for any indication of disease. Typically, netpens are checked once or twice a week by scuba divers and any dead fish (morts) are removed and examined for signs of disease (salmon die for many reasons, of which disease is just one). If the average mortality increases, fish-health specialists are called in.

DISEASE AND THE LAW

About 95 percent of all farmed salmon produced in B.C. are raised under the regular observation and care of staff or contract veterinarians. The other 5 percent call in vets as required. Almost all drugs used in B.C. are prescribed and used only by licensed veterinarians for treatment of disease on salmon farms. Only one drug can be obtained by farmers directly—oxytetracycline, when used at a maximum dose of 75 milligrams per kilogram (0.001 oz/lb) in feed for specific bacterial infections. However, because that is not an effective dose for treatment of those infections, salmon farmers seldom order it. Essentially 100 percent of the drugs used are prescribed by veterinarians.

When a veterinarian wishes to prescribe a certain drug and it is not licensed for the particular species and condition, he or she can prescribe the drug as long as there is information about the safety and efficacy of using that drug for that species. This practice is known as writing an "off-label" prescription. Off-label drugs are used because very few drugs are licensed specifically for fish. The salmon-farming industry is insignificant in size compared to land farming, so a much larger range of drugs is available to land farmers. The cost of producing and licensing a new drug can run into the tens of millions of dollars, and there simply isn't the same incentive for pharmaceutical companies to produce fish-specific products. As a result, a drug that has proven effective in treating fish may never get licensed for that use.

To obtain and keep a licence to operate, every salmon-farming company in B.C. is required to produce a Fish Health Management Plan, get it approved by MAL and put it in place. These plans outline measures to monitor for disease, to control it when it occurs and to reduce stress and maintain healthy populations. MAL is responsible for enforcing the plans. As well, each year MAL audits feed companies' drug-purchase registers to ensure that all feed that contains drugs is manufactured according to licence requirements.

In the fall of 2002, the B.C. Salmon Farmers Association (BCSFA) and MAL created the Fish Health Database, requiring salmon farmers to report all fish-health events that require veterinarian intervention. As of late 2005, 7 of the 12 major salmon farming companies—

representing 95 percent of all farmed salmon in B.C.—were providing data, and this information is available to the public through the MAL Fish Health website. To protect confidentiality, the information is compiled by region rather than company before being published. The quarterly reports posted to the website include average monthly mortality rates, a breakdown of mortality rates by causes, and the types and occurrence of all fish-health events.

MAL also audits a random selection of farm sites (over 50 percent in recent years) through its Fish Health Auditing and Surveillance Program. MAL can then evaluate the information provided through the industry database, to conduct surveillance for the occurrence of disease and to examine changes in disease trends. The program requires MAL staff to inspect farm sites and collect specimens for health evaluation and specific diseases of concern. Each year MAL and the Ministry of Environment produce a detailed public report documenting inspection and enforcement activities and compliance among salmon farms.

At the federal level, the Bureau of Veterinary Drugs—which falls under the Health Protection Branch of Health Canada—is responsible for ensuring that drugs registered and regulated in Canada are safe and effective and do not leave potentially harmful residues in food products. The bureau administers the federal *Food and Drug Act*, which authorizes certain drugs to be sold in Canada for particular species and health conditions. The federal *Feeds Act* specifies which drugs can be used in fish feeds and how to mix medicated feeds properly.

Agriculture and Agri-Food Canada regulates the use of vaccines. This function is administered by provincial authorities under a Memorandum of Understanding between the federal and provincial governments.

The federal Transplant Committee deals with the import of eggs into Canada. The movement of eggs around B.C. is regulated through a joint federal–provincial effort.

The Canadian Food Inspection Agency monitors food safety and spot-checks fish products for drug residues.

Together these regulations are designed to help prevent disease from occurring and help control it when it does. They are also designed to assure consumers that any drugs used on farmed salmon are safe for other sea life and for humans. Regulations cannot prevent disease, however. Disease is a natural part of the life cycle and it will continue to be one of the most significant concerns of the salmon-farming industry and those concerned about its impact on the aquatic environment.

WHEN FARMED SALMON ARE AFFECTED BY DISEASE, PATHOGENS ARE shed into the aquatic environment. We do not know whether those pathogens are causing more disease in wild fish. Both government and industry say there is no evidence of disease transfer from farmed to wild fish, but it is almost impossible to determine whether wild fish are being affected and to what extent.

For all of the reasons listed in this chapter, scientists consider the chances of a farmed-salmon pathogen causing a disease outbreak among wild fish to be very low. As well, no major disease event at a salmon farm in B.C. has led to problems with wild stocks. However, no conclusions can be drawn until we have baseline data regarding disease in wild fish. Wild salmon spend most of their lives in the open ocean, and only about 2 percent survive long enough to return and spawn. Much research remains to be done regarding diseases and host–pathogen relationships in the saltwater environment. In the meantime, the potential for disease transfer from farmed to wild fish cannot be discounted. As the old saying goes, the absence of proof isn't proof of absence.

7

STOWAWAYS
Sea Lice and Other Parasites

Fisheries and Oceans researchers seine for juvenile pink and chum salmon in the Broughton archipelago.

PHOTO Peter Chettleburgh

ALMOST ALL LIVING ORGANISMS, INCLUDING HUMANS, ARE HOSTS TO parasites. Parasites coexist with their hosts in relationships that have developed over millions of years, and most of them do not cause serious harm to their hosts because the host is the food supply. Salmon, both wild and farm-raised, are affected by internal and external parasites.

Many internal parasites affect salmon, and most are acquired through food. Farmed salmon rarely pick up parasites this way, because they are fed pellets that are heat-sterilized during manufacture—a process that destroys parasites. The only internal parasite that causes problems to the British Columbia salmon-farming industry is Kudoa (*Kudoa thyrsites*).

Two external parasites affect farmed salmon: sea lice, or sea louses, *Lepeophtheirus salmonis* (often simply called Leps) and *Caligus clemensi* (known as Caligus). Sea lice are a natural part of the aquatic environment and they are found on almost all wild salmonids.

INTERNAL PARASITES: KUDOA

The internal parasite *Kudoa thyrsites* is a multicellular organism distantly related to the jellyfish family that infects many aquatic fishes around the world. It is a normal part of the aquatic environment and, like other parasites, seldom causes mortality in its host. But kudoa can cause softening of the flesh after harvest, known as soft-flesh syndrome. An enzyme produced by the parasite breaks down the muscle fibre of the fish. When an affected fish is alive, it produces chemicals that mitigate the effect, but once it is dead, the parasite can thrive and the host's muscle fibre can decompose rapidly. The softened flesh is harmless to humans who eat it, but the texture makes the fish unappealing and generally unmarketable.

In B.C., farmed Atlantic salmon are much more susceptible to kudoa than wild Pacific salmon, which have apparently developed a stronger immunity to the parasite after being exposed to it for thousands of years. Kudoa is thought to be most prevalent in wild Pacific hake. Very little is known about how the disease develops or is transmitted, and there is no known treatment. Because the effects of the parasite aren't evident for several days after harvest, kudoa can be very costly to Atlantic salmon farmers.

Parasites in Humans

All humans carry and are affected by parasites, some of which are harmful and some beneficial. The harmful ones include single-celled organisms responsible for diseases such as malaria and giardiasis (beaver fever); intestinal parasites such as tapeworms, hookworms and pinworms; insect parasites such as eyebrow lice, head lice, pubic lice; mites and ticks; and fungi that cause infections such as athlete's foot. Even viruses are parasites because they cannot reproduce outside living cells. Humans get parasites from the same places fish do: food, water and close contact with a carrier. Like fish parasites, human parasites are seldom fatal.

EXTERNAL PARASITES: SEA LICE

Sea lice are crustaceans that can grow to the size of a thumb tack. They are ectoparasites—they attach to the outside of fish. Sea lice survive by consuming small amounts of their host's mucus or skin. They occur naturally in the aquatic environment throughout the world and have co-evolved with their host species.

Most adult wild salmon carry some sea lice, and the parasites also live on farmed salmon. Because sea lice are external parasites, they are not consumed by humans and do not affect the food value of their hosts.

Sea lice are normally harmless to fish. Healthy juvenile pink and chum salmon are regularly observed carrying large numbers of lice, and studies have found healthy adults returning to coastal waters to spawn with 40 or more attached to the skin of a single salmon.

Teardrop-shaped sea lice on a salmon fry.

PHOTO Alexandra Morton

However, once sea-lice numbers increase to a certain point, they can affect the health of the host. Researchers have not yet established the exact point at which this occurs, but a major Fisheries and Oceans Canada (DFO) research project to determine that benchmark for Pacific salmon was underway in 2005. The degree of impact depends on the number of lice on the host and the size and condition of the host. The initial impact is stress, which tends to weaken a host's immune system and make it more susceptible to secondary infection from other pathogens. High numbers of lice can also cause skin lesions, which can provide a route of infection for pathogens. If the infection is severe enough, it can kill the host.

In the wild there is no way to control the degree of infection. For farmed salmon, when lice loads exceed maximum levels established by the provincial government, chemicals are mixed into feed to kill the lice. Those levels are not based on a point at which the health of the salmon is affected; they are set in order to reduce the numbers of sea lice that farmed salmon shed into the aquatic environment.

Lepeophtheirus salmonis (Leps) are by far the most predominant lice because salmonids are their primary host. They are dark brown in colour and up to 18 mm (0.7 in) long. *Caligus clemensi* (Caligus) are also common in the inshore aquatic environment, but are usually much less prevalent on salmon. This species targets a wide variety of aquatic fish and can move easily to different hosts. It is light brown to yellow and up to 6 mm (0.2 in) long.

A third species, *Lepeophtheirus cuneifer*, has also been reported occasionally to be present on salmonid and non-salmonid fishes in B.C. Eight other species occur in B.C., but they are not known to affect salmonids.

LIFE CYCLE

After sea lice mate, the female produces two egg sacs that contain 100 to 500 eggs each. She can then retain sperm to produce future generations. Depending on water temperature, the eggs hatch within 5 to 15 days.

The larvae (known as nauplius) float free in the surface layers at the whim of currents for five to nine days, again depending on water temperature. During this life stage, they are unable to feed.

The lice that survive the larval stage then enter a new life stage, copepodid. These lice must find hosts and begin feeding within four to six days or they will die. At this point they move about in the top 10–20 metres (33–65 ft) of the water column, largely with the currents, but they do have a very limited ability to swim when stimulated. They use chemical and light sensors to seek out hosts, but to find hosts within four to six days is mostly a matter of chance. Lice are opportunistic—they attach to the most convenient host. Slow-swimming fish are the easiest targets. Smaller pink and chum salmon, which swim slowly and live close to the surface, have been shown to be at greater risk of infection by lice.

The copepodid attaches itself to the host's skin with a tiny filament. As the louse develops through several more life stages, it becomes able to move about the host, feeding on the mucus on its skin. Between 30 and 100 days after hatching (depending on water temperature), surviving lice become sexually mature. No one is certain of the lifespan of sea lice on a host in the wild, but research suggests that it could be as long as six months. Regardless of age, lice cannot survive on their hosts once they return to fresh water to spawn.

Life Cycle of Salmon Lice *Lepeophtheirus salmonis*

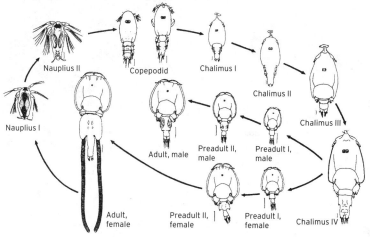

Ilustration of the life cycle of *Lepeophtheirus salmonis* (Leps). Once the eggs hatch, the lice are known as nauplius. They drift in the water column at the mercy of currents for four to six days, then transform into copepodids and have a limited ability to swim. At this stage they must find a host to feed on within about four to six days or they will die. If a host is found, the copepodid will attach to it with a filament. Then it moults through four chalimus stages, during which it stays attached. When it reaches the pre-adult stage, its legs develop and it can crawl and graze on the mucus of the host at will.

ILLUSTRATION Thomas Schram

This *Lepeophtheirus salmonis* (Leps) copepodid has just landed on a host. Within a short time it will grow a filament with which it will attach to the host.

PHOTO Eliah Kim/DFO

A second-stage Leps chalimus. Note the prominent filament.

PHOTO Eliah Kim/DFO

147

A fourth-stage female Leps chalimus. This specimen is close to the point at which it will lose its filament and be able to move at will over its host.

PHOTO Eliah Kim/DFO

An adult Leps. Note the egg strings at left. Each egg is disc-shaped.

PHOTO Paul Callow/DFO

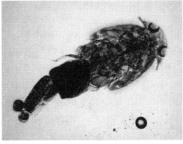

A *Caligus clemensi* (Caligus) copepodid, just after attachment to a host. Note the filament being deployed.

PHOTO Eliah Kim/DFO

Adult *Caligus* female with eggs.

PHOTO Eliah Kim/DFO

AND THEN CAME SALMON FARMS...

A salmon farm, with its large number of salmon living at high densities in open netcages, provides sea lice with a great number of potential hosts. Once a farm is infected, the lice can reproduce on the farmed salmon and shed larvae into the marine environment, which may cause infestations on wild salmon, particularly juvenile pink and chum salmon out-migrating past salmon farms on their way to sea.

Any potential impact depends first on the presence of lice on the penned fish, and then on the numbers of lice.

Farmed salmon do not always have lice. Grow-out sites are generally stocked with smolts in spring, and when they first arrive at the salt water, the smolts are coming from fresh water and therefore do not carry lice. Any lice infecting farmed fish come from sources outside the salmon farm. Depending on the location of the farm and the environmental conditions, lice begin to appear within several months. In areas known to be high in natural lice loads, salmon farmers report that it takes about a year for uninfected fish to become infected to the point that treatment is required by regulation. When those levels are reached (three mature lice per salmon during the spring pink and chum salmon outmigration in the Broughton archipelago), anti-parasite drugs are added to the feed. These drugs kill the lice on the farmed salmon and protect them against reinfection for several months. The farm is again lice-free until it is reinfected from outside sources.

Most—possibly all—salmon farms in B.C. are fallowed for several months following harvest. As it takes 15 to 24 months to raise the fish from smolts to mature adults, the farms are typically emptied every two years or less. In the absence of farmed salmon hosts, any sea-lice populations return to natural pre-farm levels.

When a salmon farm containing a million fish is infected with sea lice, even at low intensities, sea lice are added to the aquatic environment. The question is what impact those lice larvae have on wild fish during times when the farm is producing them.

Sea Lice at Salmon Farms

On the map that follows, the figures in boxes represent the average number of gravid (egg-producing) female lice per fish by area and month. Year Class 1 are fish that have been in netpens less than one year. Year Class 2 are fish that have been in netpens more than 1 year. These numbers are as reported by salmon farms and spot-checked by provincial regulators. The numbers do not show whether the fish have been treated for sea lice.

As the figures show, between October 2003 and June 2005, over the entire B.C. coast, there was an average of less than one adult female sea louse per farmed Atlantic salmon. The exception is the Broughton archipelago, where there was an average of 0.5 lice on fish in Year Class 1 and just under two lice for fish on Year Class 2.

ABUNDANCE OF SEA LICE AT SALMON FARMS
(by Month Within Established Fish Health Surveillance Zones)

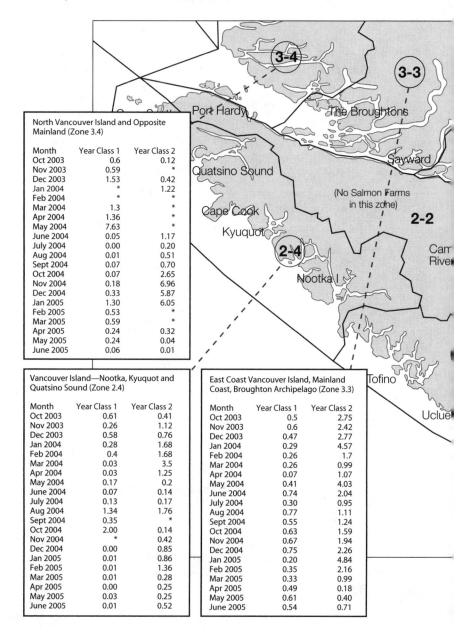

North Vancouver Island and Opposite Mainland (Zone 3.4)

Month	Year Class 1	Year Class 2
Oct 2003	0.6	0.12
Nov 2003	0.59	*
Dec 2003	1.53	0.42
Jan 2004	*	1.22
Feb 2004	*	*
Mar 2004	1.3	*
Apr 2004	1.36	*
May 2004	7.63	*
June 2004	0.05	1.17
July 2004	0.00	0.20
Aug 2004	0.01	0.51
Sept 2004	0.07	0.70
Oct 2004	0.07	2.65
Nov 2004	0.18	6.96
Dec 2004	0.33	5.87
Jan 2005	1.30	6.05
Feb 2005	0.53	*
Mar 2005	0.59	*
Apr 2005	0.24	0.32
May 2005	0.24	0.04
June 2005	0.06	0.01

(No Salmon Farms in this zone)

Vancouver Island—Nootka, Kyuquot and Quatsino Sound (Zone 2.4)

Month	Year Class 1	Year Class 2
Oct 2003	0.61	0.41
Nov 2003	0.26	1.12
Dec 2003	0.58	0.76
Jan 2004	0.28	1.68
Feb 2004	0.4	1.68
Mar 2004	0.03	3.5
Apr 2004	0.03	1.25
May 2004	0.17	0.2
June 2004	0.07	0.14
July 2004	0.13	0.17
Aug 2004	1.34	1.76
Sept 2004	0.35	*
Oct 2004	2.00	0.14
Nov 2004	*	0.42
Dec 2004	0.00	0.85
Jan 2005	0.01	0.86
Feb 2005	0.01	1.36
Mar 2005	0.01	0.28
Apr 2005	0.00	0.25
May 2005	0.03	0.25
June 2005	0.01	0.52

East Coast Vancouver Island, Mainland Coast, Broughton Archipelago (Zone 3.3)

Month	Year Class 1	Year Class 2
Oct 2003	0.5	2.75
Nov 2003	0.6	2.42
Dec 2003	0.47	2.77
Jan 2004	0.29	4.57
Feb 2004	0.26	1.7
Mar 2004	0.26	0.99
Apr 2004	0.07	1.07
May 2004	0.41	4.03
June 2004	0.74	2.04
July 2004	0.30	0.95
Aug 2004	0.77	1.11
Sept 2004	0.55	1.24
Oct 2004	0.63	1.59
Nov 2004	0.67	1.94
Dec 2004	0.75	2.26
Jan 2005	0.20	4.84
Feb 2005	0.35	2.16
Mar 2005	0.33	0.99
Apr 2005	0.49	0.18
May 2005	0.61	0.40
June 2005	0.54	0.71

East Coast Vancouver Island, Campbell River, Johnstone Strait, Mainland Coast (Zone 3.2)

Month	Year Class 1	Year Class 2
Oct 2003	0.88	1.58
Nov 2003	*	*
Dec 2003	0.02	4.85
Jan 2004	0.03	*
Feb 2004	0.0	2.2
Mar 2004	0.25	0.0
Apr 2004	0.21	0.4
May 2004	0.16	0.4
June 2004	0.21	0.35
July 2004	0.23	0.50
Aug 2004	0.38	0.65
Sept 2004	0.10	0.50
Oct 2004	0.04	0.50
Nov 2004	0.07	0.60
Dec 2004	0.12	0.00
Jan 2005	0.48	0.05
Feb 2005	0.03	0.50
Mar 2005	0.18	0.88
Apr 2005	0.22	1.82
May 2005	0.38	0.58
June 2005	0.45	0.13

Coast—Sunshine Coast (Zone 3.1)

Month	Year Class 1	Year Class 2
Oct 2003	0.14	1.17
Nov 2003	0.63	*
Dec 2003	*	0.42
Jan 2004	0.0	0.7
Feb 2004	*	0.4
Mar 2004	*	0.2
Apr 2004	0.01	0.74
May 2004	0.0	0.4
June 2004	0.05	0.95
July 2004	0.45	1.20
Aug 2004	0.04	0.08
Sept 2004	0.10	0.00
Oct 2004	0.10	*
Nov 2004	0.03	0.02
Dec 2004	0.02	0.09
Jan 2005	0.00	1.67
Feb 2005	0.02	0.07
Mar 2005	0.02	0.01
Apr 2005	0.03	0.07
May 2005	0.08	0.12
June 2005	0.10	0.06

Vancouver Island—Clayoquot Sound, South Vancouver Island (Zone 2.3)

Month	Year Class 1	Year Class 2
Oct 2003	0.09	0.13
Nov 2003	0.00	2.00
Dec 2003	*	2.05
Jan 2004	0.42	0.72
Feb 2004	0.00	1.05
Mar 2004	0.10	1.45
Apr 2004	0.08	0.07
May 2004	*	0.05
June 2004	0.95	0.53
July 2004	0.40	*
Aug 2004	1.55	*
Sept 2004	0.03	*
Oct 2004	0.02	0.63
Nov 2004	0.11	0.00
Dec 2004	0.18	0.02
Jan 2005	0.32	0.18
Feb 2005	0.85	2.13
Mar 2005	0.59	1.30
Apr 2005	0.20	0.54
May 2005	0.42	0.00
June 2005	0.12	0.07

3-2

3-1

2-1

Nanaimo

Vancouver

(No Salmon Farms in this zone)

nfield

Port Renfrew

Victoria

*Count is missing for one or more of these reasons:
  ◆ site is fallow
  ◆ site is harvesting and fewer than 3 pens left on site
  ◆ smolt entry and fewer than 3 pens on site, or 1 month since third smolt pen entered
  ◆ fish being treated for sea lice
  ◆ fish being treated/managed for other health problems
  ◆ fish could not be handled due to other environmental concerns
Note: There is no reporting for Zone 2.1 (East Coast Vancouver Island—Victoria to Comox) or Zone 2.2 (East Coast Vancouver Island—Courtenay to Port Hardy) because there are no salmon farms in those zones.
Source: B.C. Ministry of Agriculture and Lands/B.C. Salmon Farmers Association, Fish Health Database website.

WHEN A FARM BECOMES INFECTED

Environmental conditions such as current, salinity and temperature play a major role in the abundance of sea lice. Current is the most significant factor in the dispersal of larvae and copepodids. Salinity affects the survival of lice at all stages: the lower the salinity, the lower their rates of survival. Water temperature controls the speed at which lice grow: the warmer the temperature, the faster they grow and reproduce. As well, when there are more hosts to reproduce on, there are more sea lice; where there are fewer, the numbers decline. DFO researchers believe that because farmed salmon get lice from wild fish, and because they live in the same waters and environmental conditions as wild fish, sea-lice abundance on salmon farms parallels lice dynamics outside the farm.

For example, in the Broughton archipelago, the annual spring runoff from the snowpack on adjacent mainland mountains is funnelled into the mainland inlets and rivers of the Broughtons. This runoff forms a low-salinity layer over the normal sea water and can reduce surface salinity enough to depress sea-lice productivity throughout the entire area. In years of average to good snowpack, the surface layer has actually eliminated sea lice at many of the 14 or so salmon farms operating in the Broughtons. Lice populations outside the farms are thought to be reduced as well.

For salmon farms located near wild salmon runs, infection of farmed fish often begins when returning wild salmon pass by in the late summer and fall and shed the lice loads they've picked up during their time offshore. Salmon farmers often report a "pulse" of sea lice at those times, and sea-lice numbers are probably higher all the way along the route to their spawning grounds.

Atlantic salmon are more susceptible to sea lice than Pacific salmon, probably because they are slower swimmers. Stressed and diseased fish also swim more slowly and become easy targets for lice.

Salmon farms are typically sited in areas with current running at ½–3 knots, which provides a steady supply of oxygenated water and helps to disperse fish waste. Those currents ebb and flood with the tides. They are also influenced by freshwater runoff from nearby inlets, which in the Broughton archipelago, for example, causes an overall westward drift of the surface layer. A recent combined industry/DFO study on the hydrography of the Broughtons measured the average net outflow at 1.7 kilometres (1 mi) per day. That means lice larvae are likely to be carried 8.5–15 kilomtres (5–9 mi) downcurrent from the farm where they were hatched before they are able to attach to a host. From this point, they can infect fish for another four to six days, during which time they will be carried about another 7–10 kilometres (4–6 mi) downcurrent. The geography of this area is complex and the study's findings aren't likely to be repeated exactly, but the general conclusion is that any infection of wild fish is likely to occur at some distance from the salmon farm of origin—meaning that the least likely source of lice infections at a salmon farm is its own fish. When the incidence of lice rises at a salmon farm, it is because of gradual recruitment of sea lice from wild fish or from another salmon farm a few kilometres upcurrent.

This conclusion is consistent with observations of salmon farmers. If sea lice were constantly reinfecting the site at which they hatched, lice levels at the site would rise consistently and exponentially. The salmon at the farm could be overwhelmed within several months and the farm would be forced to treat its population constantly to get rid of the lice. That is not the case. As the sidebar "Abundance of Sea Lice at B.C. Salmon Farms" shows, sea-lice levels vary throughout B.C., but the average is less than one reproductive female louse per fish throughout the entire grow-out cycle.

However, a 2003 study published in the *Proceedings of the Royal Society of London* came up with a different set of data. That study looked at lice infestations of pink and chum salmon as they outmigrated from their natal streams, past a salmon farm in the Broughtons and down their migration corridors, a distance of some 60 kilometres (36 mi). The authors, Krkosek et al., found that the juvenile salmon carried almost no sea lice before encountering the farm, but once they passed nearby, they immediately became infected at levels about 70 times greater than ambient levels. The study also found that once the lice were transferred, they matured and reproduced on the juvenile salmon and the second-generation lice reinfected the salmon at a point 30 kilometres (18 mi) downcurrent. They concluded that lice levels downcurrent of the farm exceeded natural background levels for approximately 75 kilometres (45 mi). The authors reported that "within a salmon farming region, most lice on wild juvenile pink and chum salmon originated from farmed salmon" and that "salmon aquaculture likely has negative impacts on wild salmon populations." The study did not examine whether those "extra" lice caused the wild salmon any ill effects.

Critics of the study pointed out that it takes five to nine days for lice larvae to reach the infective stage, and during that time surface currents would carry them well downcurrent and away from the salmon farms. The authors agreed that the area they studied has a net outward flow, but suggested the narrowness of the inlets and the large tidal currents could have allowed the larvae to stay near the farm for several days. During the study, however, salmon farmers reported that lice remained at normal levels. If the wild salmon were being infected adjacent to the farm site, lice levels at the farm should have increased in parallel. They did not, which suggests that the infection originated from natural sources of sea lice farther up the inlet. *why would they increase?*

Clearly a great deal more research is needed to identify sources of infection and the impact on wild fish.

always the authors' answer when the results don't favor the farms.

MEASURING THE IMPACT

Regardless of the numbers of lice shed by farmed salmon, the impact of any increase above normal levels depends on the same factors that affect sea lice outside of the farm environment. These factors include the ability of the planktonic-stage lice to survive and their ability to find a host within the few days they have to do so. And once salmon are infected—whether wild or farmed—the lice may or may not compromise the health of the host.

Lice begin to infect wild salmon smolts as soon as they leave fresh water. Pink and chum smolts are known to become heavily infested during the weeks or months when they remain in shallow nearshore waters before migrating offshore. Because they enter the salt water almost immediately after emerging from the gravel, pink—and, to a slightly lesser extent, chum—are initially much smaller than other Pacific salmon, which can put them more at risk for lice than other species.

On a fish of any size, the number of lice that is lethal depends on the size of the smolt, the health of the smolt, the infection rate and other factors. There is no doubt that lice can kill a juvenile salmon, but there is no consensus on the lethal threshold for Pacific salmon. Laboratory studies on juvenile Atlantic salmon and sea trout (European sea-run brown trout) in Europe suggest that 1.6 lice per gram (0.04 oz) of fish weight (based on a 60 gram/2 oz smolt), can kill the individual. DFO scientists do not believe that lethal load numbers for Atlantic salmon are the same as for Pacific salmon, which have a different genetic makeup and completely different life history. Studies were underway in 2005, but there is no published data on the number of lice that can kill a juvenile Pacific salmon. Researchers here say it is common to see healthy Pacific salmon with 5 to 10 times the loads cited as lethal for Atlantic salmon. As well, when pink and chum salmon smolts first enter salt water, they typically double in weight every 14 days, compared to 100 days for Atlantic salmon. In the time it takes copepodid lice to reach maturity once they have attached to the smolt, the fish has the opportunity to grow considerably in size, lessening the impact of any lice that mature.

Once salmon smolts leave the nearshore environment, they spend a year or more offshore before returning to their natal streams to spawn. Virtually all returning salmon are carrying sea lice. A DFO study, *Sea Lice on Adult Pacific Salmon in the Coastal Waters of Central British Columbia, Canada*, by Beamish et al., published in 2005, reported that every returning pink, chum and sockeye salmon examined had sea lice, with an average of 41.5–53 lice on every fish. One pink salmon carried 203 and one chum had 302. Most of the salmon had minimal skin damage or scale loss as a result of the lice.

In the late summer and fall, when lice-laden salmon are returning to spawn, they are unlikely to be hurt if they pick up copepodid-stage lice because they are about to enter fresh water, where the lice will not survive. In winter, when there are fewer salmonid and other hosts, the great majority of lice shed by salmon farms likely will not survive—unless currents carry them to another stocked salmon farm while they are in their copepodid infective stage.

However, when conditions allow, salmon farms contribute large numbers of lice to the aquatic environment. We do not know what effect those lice have. It stands to reason that any addition of lice to our waters has the potential to upset the natural sea lice–host balance that has evolved over thousands of years.

yes we do!
see above

Lice Epidemics in the Wild

We know that wild adult salmon tend to become more heavily infested with lice during late summer and fall, when they have to mill about in the shallow, warmer water at river mouths, waiting for the fall rains to raise water levels in the river. This was documented in two separate incidents that took place at the head of Alberni Inlet on the west coast of Vancouver Island. In both cases, large numbers of returning sockeye were stalled by low water at the entrance to the Somass River. The lice carried by the returning sockeye reproduced very quickly in the warm, shallow water. Infestation rates skyrocketed and large numbers of salmon died before they could spawn. The first incident took place in the 1970s, before there were salmon farms in the area, and the second in the 1990s, when salmon farms were operating in the area. In the latter event, the sockeye carried an average of 300 lice per fish, and some carried as many as 1,300. Heavy lice outbreaks have also been reported among fish returning to the Fraser River to spawn.

THE OVERWINTERING QUESTION

Some 10 to 40 million Pacific salmon return to the Broughtons each year or pass through the area, and large numbers of sea lice, both the Leps and Caligus species, are transported into the region. Historically, DFO scientists believed that in the absence of salmon farms, those lice died when the salmon entered freshwater streams to spawn. Any lice that were shed before the fish entered fresh water were also thought to die because they had no hosts—particularly Leps, which are generally dominant on salmonids and were once thought to infect only salmonids. If this were true, sea-lice numbers would plummet in winter and not be present to infect outmigrating salmon smolts entering salt water in spring.

Because salmon farms provide such a great number of hosts that would not be there otherwise, the question arises as to whether salmon farms provide unnatural overwintering habitat for sea lice, upsetting the natural annual life cycles of lice and hosts and increasing lice populations all year round.

Little scientific data is available on how lice overwinter, but we know that sea lice survived for many thousands of years before the appearance of salmon farms, so they must be able to reproduce over the winter. We also know that returning adult wild salmon have spent a year or more in the open ocean and, based on the lifespan of sea lice and the large numbers of lice on returning salmon, that sea lice are reproducing and reinfecting wild salmon in offshore waters in sufficient numbers to maintain an offshore population.

However, that does not explain how lice, especially Leps, overwinter in nearshore waters so that they can infect outmigrating smolts in spring. DFO scientists are only now beginning to gain an understanding of those dynamics. For example, a DFO study published in 2005 showed that Leps do not infect only salmonids. The study found that 80 percent of the sticklebacks captured in the Broughtons were carrying lice (an average of 19 per fish) of both the *Lepeophtheirus salmonis* and *Caligus clemensi* species. This was the first solid proof that there were overwintering hosts for Leps.

It is also believed that—in the absence of salmon farms and in addition to sticklebacks—enough salmonids remain in the nearshore waters through the winter to sustain populations of Leps. Populations of cutthroat trout, steelhead, immature coho, chinook salmon and Dolly Varden stay in the Broughtons all year round, but their numbers and the extent of their role as hosts to overwintering lice is unknown. It is possible that lice overwintering on these species are genetically programmed to hatch as a supply of new hosts—pink and chum salmon—exit their natal streams in spring.

Another possibility proposed by DFO researchers is that the larvae that infect outmigrating salmon may originate from adult salmon egg strings that fell off returning salmon in the previous season. The larvae may remain dormant until environmental conditions associated with spring cue the eggs to hatch. So far this is only speculation in the case of sea lice, but many marine planktonic species—including copepods—are known to be active during seasons when food is abundant and to spend the rest of the year in a resting or hibernation stage.

Not everyone agrees that Leps overwinter on hosts. Biologist Alexandra Morton theorizes that all sea lice carried to nearshore waters by spawning salmon die when their hosts enter fresh water. She says that there are no historic overwintering populations of *L. salmonis* in nearshore waters of the Broughton archipelago and that before salmon farms, juvenile salmon did not become infected until they left nearshore waters. If this is true, all the lice on juvenile pink salmon must have come from salmon farms, which would contain the only nearshore overwintering hosts for this species.

There is less mystery about how Caligus lice overwinter. Caligus are non-specific parasites that live on a number of year-round inshore residents, including stickleback and herring as well as salmonids. This was shown by the 2005 DFO study that found sticklebacks carrying very large numbers of both Caligus and Leps.

In some years Caligus are found in greater numbers than Leps on juvenile pink and chum salmon. But Caligus usually represents less than 50 percent of the lice load on juvenile salmon. They are also found on farmed salmon, but in lower numbers than on wild juvenile salmon, for unknown reasons. Salmon farms likely contribute to the overall abundance of Caligus, but that species probably does not have the same overwintering challenges as Leps.

SEA LICE IN OTHER COUNTRIES

Little research has been done in B.C. on the interactions between sea lice, salmon farms and wild fish, but numerous studies have taken place in Europe, where the salmon-farming industry has been active longer. The European studies are useful for reference but cannot be compared directly to the B.C. situation.

In Europe, there is a far larger biomass of farmed salmon compared to wild salmon. Norway, for example, has about 120 times more farmed salmon than wild salmon. Therefore, farmed salmon dominate lice production in the aquatic environment. In B.C. there are far more wild salmon than farmed salmon, they are spread over a much larger area and they return to many more rivers. Therefore, wild salmon dominate lice production throughout B.C. coastal waters.

A stickleback with a high abundance of both *Lepeoph-theirus* and *Caligus* species of lice shows that salmonids are not the exclusive hosts to *Lepeophtheirus*, as once thought.

PHOTO Ted Sweeten/DFO

As well, European research is based on studies of Atlantic salmon smolts. Pacific salmon smolts are very different. In Europe, both farmed fish and wild salmonids are the genus *Salmo* (Atlantic salmon and brown trout). In B.C., wild Pacific salmonids are of the genus *Oncorhynchus*, whereas 80 percent of farmed fish are *Salmo*. The growth dynamics of Pacific salmon are quite different than for Atlantic salmon, as are lice dynamics, though the *L. salmonis* species of lice occurs in both oceans. For example, pink and chum salmon smolts enter sea water at about 1 gram (0.04 oz) in weight and can double their weight in 14 days. Atlantic salmon smolts enter sea water at 30 to 50 grams (1–1.8 oz), and it takes them about 100 days to double their weight. The rapidly increasing body weight of pink and chum salmon diffuses the impact of a fixed number of lice. For example, a Pacific salmon that is infected by five copepodid stage lice increases in size between two and eight times before the lice become sexually mature adults.

European researchers developed a lethal load model in the laboratory suggesting that an infection of 1.6 lice per gram (0.04 oz) of host weight could cause death in sea trout smolts weighing 60 grams (2 oz). This model cannot be applied to the much smaller Pacific salmon smolts, because researchers in B.C. regularly document juvenile salmon in fine health that are carrying 5 to 10 times as many lice as would kill the larger European sea trout smolt.

B.C. has milder year-round water temperatures, which speed up the life cycle of lice, and a much higher number and variety of hosts, so it is likely many more lice are produced naturally here than in Europe.

However, although there are significant differences in that farmed salmon greatly outnumber wild salmon in Europe and therefore dominate sea-lice dynamics and abundance, some parallels can be drawn.

In Europe, sea lice are such a problem to salmon farmers in Norway, Scotland and Ireland that regular treatments are needed to control the lice. Several European studies have shown a significant correlation between lice infections in wild salmon and at nearby salmon farms. In some areas, wild fish near farms had 10 to 20 times more lice than wild fish living in areas without farms. In addition, lethal infestations of lice in wild fish were said to be occurring only in the vicinity of salmon farms. To make matters worse, no effective methods for treatment were available at the time these conditions were present.

In October 2002, *National Geographic News* reported that scientists· in Scotland had found a direct link between the explosion of sea lice in farmed fish and the decline of Scottish sea trout. Another study, carried out over two years in the western Highlands of Scotland, found that sea-lice levels rose from 0 to 75 percent during the second year of a farm's production. In 2003, researchers in Norway, at the University of Bergen and the Institute of Aquatic Research, found that up to 86 percent of young wild salmon in fjords that contained fish farms were dying from lice infestations.

Like B.C., European countries have government regulations that control sea lice in farms. In Norway, treatment is required when levels reach 0.5 lice per gravid (egg-bearing) female, or four total (motile) lice from December to July, and two lice per gravid female, or 10 total motile lice in summer. These numbers are not related to lethal levels. The goal is to reduce the numbers of lice spreading from farms to the wild, based on the potential impacts to very low numbers of wild salmon in Norway.

TO TREAT OR NOT TO TREAT

As part of a salmon farm's health-management practice, the population is regularly monitored for disease and parasites. Most salmon farms in B.C. have consistently low lice levels, and the salmon never require treatment for lice. This is especially true on farms raising chinook and/or coho salmon, which have a much higher resistance to sea lice. As well, different areas of the coast have different natural levels of sea lice.

Little data is available on the historical prevalence of sea lice on farmed salmon in B.C. A 1991 report prepared for the B.C. Aquaculture Research and Development Council detailed a survey of 17 salmon farms in B.C. Seven of those farms had at one time experienced health problems and/or mortalities from sea lice. Five of them had treated their fish to eliminate the lice.

Stolt Sea Farms, one of B.C.'s largest salmon-farming companies (now merged with Marine Harvest Canada), has raised 60 crops of farmed salmon (mostly in the Broughton archipelago) over the past 15 years, and until the Sea Lice Monitoring Program was implemented, they say they had treated the fish for lice a total of 15 times. Heritage Salmon (now Mainstream Canada), the other major player in the Broughtons, reported that they did not have to treat any of their fish for lice between the late 1980s and most of the 1990s. The small numbers of lice that overwintered on their fish were eliminated in the spring, when freshwater runoff reduced the salinity of the water and the lice died. More recently, Stolt reported that they have had to carry out occasional treatment, particularly in seasons with low snowpacks and therefore less runoff.

Before the Sea Lice Monitoring Program, salmon farms treated their fish only when lice levels rose to the point where they began to affect the fish. In such cases, which were rare, the salmon farmer could either harvest the fish or treat them to kill the lice. Lice levels are almost always highest on larger fish, which are closer to market size and nearly ready to be harvested anyway. Other fish could be treated with anti-parasite chemicals. The farm would then be lice-free until it was restocked or reinfected by wild salmonids.

MANDATORY SEA-LICE MONITORING

Until 2003, there was no standard method of evaluating, identifying or reporting the lice stages on farmed fish, and farm staff were largely untrained in this area. Sea-lice abundance at salmon farms was proprietary information—not shared with other salmon-farming companies or the public.

In 2003, the provincial Ministry of Agriculture, Food and Fisheries (later Ministry of Agriculture and Lands, or MAL) introduced the Sea Lice Action Plan, largely to address concerns raised by critics of salmon farming about the impact on wild fish of sea lice from salmon farms. The plan was designed to improve research into sea lice and to train farm staff to identify and sample sea lice.

Early that year, the government implemented the Interim Sea Lice Monitoring Program for salmon farms in the Broughton archipelago, the coast area with the highest numbers of lice. Officials wanted to collect information on levels of sea lice at salmon farms and to work with industry to develop management plans to minimize the levels of lice during the outmigration of wild pink and chum salmon smolts. In 2004 the monitoring program was extended to include mandatory monitoring of sea lice on all salmon farms in B.C. Salmon farms must now be sampled for sea lice monthly at Atlantic salmon sites, and quarterly at Pacific salmon sites (these fish are less susceptible). The results are reported to MAL and verified by random on-site sampling and auditing (of 25 percent of the farms each quarter) by ministry inspectors. Those numbers are collated and reported quarterly on MAL's Fish Health website, which is public. The program is designed to provide both public accountability and to assist in sea-lice research.

The program has set action levels that must be taken by salmon farmers when sea-lice levels exceed three motile (all stages) lice during periods of juvenile outmigration. During the rest of the year, the trigger is six motile lice. Treatment or harvesting is mandatory when those levels are reached.

Now that fish are being treated more often, the use of anti-parasitic drugs is increasing. No one knows whether the new treatment levels are appropriate, or whether the more frequent use of anti-parasitic chemicals is more harmful than a less vigilant approach to lice.

In the absence of abundant freshwater runoff, fish may now be subjected to one or two courses of treatment during the 15 to 24 months they live in their netcages. According to Marine Harvest, the new trigger levels will require 90 treatments over the next 15 years, compared to 15 treatments over the past 15 years.

TREATMENT

Prior to the introduction of Atlantic salmon in the mid-1980s, there was seldom—if ever—a need to treat Pacific salmon for sea lice. Sea lice simply weren't accumulating in significant numbers on Pacific salmon in the netpens, and therefore treatment wasn't required. However, Atlantic salmon weren't as resistant, and when necessary, bath treatments were used to remove lice. This involved placing large tarps around the netpens and pouring in pesticides. Several chemicals were tried until about 1988, when a new product, ivermectin, which could be added to fish feed and was safer and much more effective, made bath treatments obsolete. Today, veterinarians can prescribe ivermectin or emamectin benzoate. Both are pesticides, but in Canada they are registered as drugs because they are administered in feed. Like all chemical pesticides, they are toxic.

Ivermectin

Ivermectin is not formulated specifically for fish, but is widely used to treat domestic and farm animals for parasites and can also be used on humans. It is effective in killing sea lice, but laboratory studies have shown that it may harm other crustaceans and marine life. It is still legal to use ivermectin, but it has not been used on a salmon farm in B.C. since 2000 because emamectin benzoate is more effective.

Emamectin benzoate (SLICE)

Emamectin benzoate—trade name SLICE—has proven much more effective than ivermectin. It is approved for use as a pesticide in the U.S. and Japan for crops such as leafy vegetables, turnip greens, cottonseed and fruiting vegetables, and in products such as tomato paste. It is also used to treat lice. Unlike ivermectin, SLICE was formulated specially for farmed salmon. It is mixed with feed in a proportion of 2–5 kilograms per tonne (4–11 lbs/ton), with an active component of 2 percent. It is reported to kill all stages of sea lice within 2 to 4 weeks and to prevent reinfection for up to 14 weeks. One round of treatment costs about $100,000.

SLICE is currently awaiting approval by Health Canada, though it is approved for use on fish in many other countries. Meanwhile, it is being used under Health Canada's Emergency Drug Release Program. To obtain SLICE, the veterinarian must apply to the Veterinary Drugs Directorate (VDD) with details of the group of fish requiring treatment. If VDD accepts the application, it approves release of the specific amount for that treatment, and the drug is shipped directly to the feed company to be mixed with the feed as specified on the veterinarian's prescription. After treatment the veterinarian must provide a follow-up report to the VDD with treatment information, including clinical observations and any adverse reactions that were noted. In B.C., the total amount of SLICE used on salmon farms each year is less than 10 kilograms (22 lbs).

Once fish are treated with SLICE, 90 percent of the chemical is absorbed immediately into the skin. About 10 percent passes out in feces right away and the balance is excreted slowly thereafter. Fish treated with emamectin benzoate must go through a minimum withdrawal period of 25 days (at 10°C, longer in colder water) before they are harvested to ensure they are drug-free. Withdrawal times in both Canada and the U.S. are stricter than in countries where the drug has already been approved. In the U.K. and Chile, there is a zero-day withdrawal time. In Norway the withdrawal time is 17.5 days (at 10°C water temperature).

As with any drug treatment, there is the possibility that lice will develop resistance. Only one treatment for lice is in use at this time, so there is an even higher probability that the drug will kill off the susceptible parasites and leave the resistant ones. On the other hand, in B.C. the fact that large populations of sea lice on wild fish can replenish the pool of parasites on farmed fish actually hinders the development of resistance. According to Dr. John F. Burka of the Department of Biomedical Sciences at Atlantic Veterinary College, there have been no reports of lice developing resistance in any jurisdiction where SLICE is used.

Prescribing vets are required to contact the Canadian Food Inspection Agency (CFIA) prior to the harvest of any population that has been treated with emamectin benzoate. The CFIA inspects those fish to ensure that they do not contain harmful residues. The federal Veterinary Drugs Directorate has set a maximum residue limit of 50 ppb in harvested fish tissue. This compares to 100 ppb allowed in Europe, the U.K. and Chile. According to the Association of Aquaculture Veterinarians of B.C., a large proportion of the 100 or so samples taken annually from treated fish test negative for emamectin benzoate, and of those that are positive, none has exceeded Health Canada's limits.

In 1999 the Scottish Environment Protection Agency—a fish-farm advisory group—reviewed the environmental risks of emamectin benzoate and found that used properly, it should result in no unacceptable damage to the environment. Their field studies, and those in B.C. by the well-known environmental impact expert Stephen Cross, showed that emamectin benzoate was not detected in the water column during the treatment of Atlantic salmon, even at the netcage perimeter. The SEPA research found that before and after treatment, accumulations of emamectin benzoate in crustaceans, molluscs and fish near salmon farms were well below concentrations at which any measurable effects could be observed.

SEPA analyzed sediments under Scottish netpens and found that 89 percent of the sites under or near fish farms contained no residues of chemicals used to treat sea lice. They also found no effects on sediment-dwelling aquatic life from the use of emamectin benzoate.

Several groups, including Watershed Watch and the Raincoast Conservation Society, quote a study on the effects of emamectin benzoate (Waldy et al.) that found the chemical induces premature moulting in lobsters and has caused female lobsters to lose their eggs prematurely. However, lobsters are not native to the west coast, and the lobsters tested were force-fed at 10 times the rate they would feed during normal treatment of farmed Atlantic salmon. If farmed salmon were given that kind of dose, they would probably die.

In B.C., DFO researchers studied the effects of emamectin benzoate on adult spot prawns and Dungeness crabs at concentrations equal to those they would accumulate during treatment of farmed salmon. The researchers were well aware that prawn fishermen use the standard salmon-feed pellets for feed in their traps, but they found that both species avoided salmon-feed pellets, whether treated with SLICE or not. They also found that no crabs or prawns died as a result of the treatment.

In the best of all worlds, no chemicals—especially those formulated to be toxic—would be introduced into the aquatic environment. As long as salmon farms operate in the province, British Columbians must decide which is the lesser of two evils: sea lice or emamectin benzoate.

Pesticide Use on Land

Without pesticides it is often very difficult for land farmers to produce sufficient crops. The pesticides used in crop and animal farming—herbicides, insecticides, fungicides—are poisons by definition. Residues of chemicals such as DDT, heptachlor, dieldrin and toxaphene (all now banned in Canada) that have been applied to crops intentionally are believed to be present in the tissues of most people on earth.

Canada spreads about 34 million kilograms (37,400 tons) of pesticides over 35 million hectares (87.5 million acres) every year—or 1 kilogram (2.2 lbs) of pesticide per Canadian, per year. The area over which it is used is 11 times larger than Vancouver Island. The amount of pesticide used in Canada is only a fraction of the 450 million kilograms (495,000 tons) used annually in the U.S.A.

THE BROUGHTON CONTROVERSY

Every year salmon return to spawn in seven major and several smaller rivers within the 400 square kilometre (160 sq mi) Broughton archipelago. Pink and chum salmon are the most predominant species and their populations have historically been strong. Until salmon farms appeared about 20 years ago, little development had taken place in these waters other than logging and commercial fishing. Salmon farming is now the dominant industry. On average, about half of the 26 salmon farms in the Broughtons are operating at any given time.

Pink and chum salmon spawn in fall and their offspring hatch in spring. Juveniles of both species outmigrate to the salt water almost immediately. At about 3.5 centimetres (1.5 in) in length, pink salmon are the smallest of the Pacific salmon when they reach salt water. Pinks return to their home streams to spawn in the fall of their second year, and chum return after three to five years. Runs of pink salmon in the Broughtons are generally much larger during even years.

THE BEGINNING: 2001

In 2001, Alexandra Morton, an independent biologist and a long-time vocal opponent of salmon farming, was alerted by friends that they were finding pink salmon smolts in the Broughtons covered in lice. She began to investigate. In June and July of that year she used a dipnet to collect almost 1,000 juvenile pink salmon from 48 sites around the Broughtons.

These pink were among millions migrating to the open ocean. They were the offspring of a record return of 3.6 million pink to the Broughtons in 2000, and they would return to spawn in the fall of 2002.

SALMON FARM LOCATIONS IN THE BROUGHTON ARCHIPELAGO

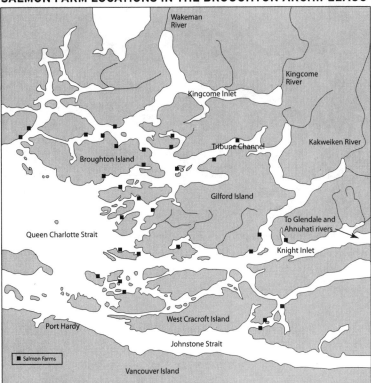

Locations of fish farms in the Broughtons in fall 2005, and the major river systems that drain into the area.

Morton reported that over 75 percent of the fish she sampled had high loads of lice—an average of 11.2 lice per fish. She also found significantly more lice on fish sampled near salmon farms than on fish that had not yet migrated past the farms. Assuming no natural sources of sea lice in the Broughtons, she began to suspect that salmon at farms in the area might be acting as reservoirs for the lice, and the offspring of those lice were spreading to juvenile pink and chum. Morton warned that the severe infestations she had documented could result in a collapse of the pink salmon run the following year when they returned to spawn.

Alexandra Morton, a biologist and whale researcher, has been the strongest critic of salmon farming in the Broughtons. Most of her research sampling to date has been done with the use of dipnets, but she began to use a beach seine for sampling (shown here) in 2004.

PHOTO Ursula Meissner

Until that time no one had done any significant research on natural background levels of sea lice in the Broughtons, or anywhere else on the B.C. coast. However, in 1964, DFO researchers recorded an infestation of pink salmon smolts with Caligus and a lesser number of Leps. This led to the naming of *Caligus clemensi*, a previously unidentified species of Caligus. This was all we had in the way of background levels of sea life in the Broughton area. Without much more of such data, it is impossible to judge the impact of salmon farming on natural sea-lice levels in juvenile pink and chum salmon.

Her findings set off alarm bells for Morton and several environmental groups. In response, DFO undertook its own investigation later that summer. Researchers boarded a purse seiner and a trawler, and they sampled juvenile pink and chum salmon in the area. They found that 58 percent of the fish surveyed had lice, and that the average fish had 1.7 lice, significantly fewer than Morton's findings of 11.2.

DFO compared these results to a 1991 study of lice on larger salmon caught in the open ocean. That study found that 90 percent of pink salmon surveyed carried an average of six lice, and 45 percent of the chum salmon had an average of just over two lice. The number of lice they found on juvenile salmon in the Broughton area was average compared to the lice levels on wild adult fish in the open ocean. Morton and others responded by saying that the timing, location and suitability of the trawl and seine sampling gear used by DFO did not provide an accurate comparison to her findings. The DFO study was largely discredited, though others pointed out that Morton's use of dipnets introduced a bias to her numbers and that her findings should be discredited as well.

To use a dipnet, one must first spot individual fish or groups, then attempt to catch them by scooping them up. Only the fish that are caught in the dipnet are examined, and those fish may not be representative of the average population. Weakened and sick fish are typically slower swimmers that cannot escape as readily as healthy, robust fish. Slow swimmers are also most likely to be infected by sea lice. Therefore, individuals that can be caught with dipnets are much more likely to have lice.

Meanwhile, in the fall of 2001 there was a record return of 1.5 million "odd-year" pink salmon to the Broughtons—the highest return in recorded history. Morton's warning that lice could compromise the size of the run had not nearly come true.

THE COLLAPSE: 2002

In the spring of 2002, Alexandra Morton again sampled outmigrating juvenile pink and chum. She captured just over 1,000 fish and found an average of 4.1 lice per fish, significantly less than the 11.2 of the previous year. As well, she once again observed higher numbers of lice on the salmon she collected near salmon farms.

In the fall of 2002, pink salmon returns to the Broughtons fell to their lowest even-year levels in a decade. After a record 3.6 million pink had returned two years earlier, fewer than 120,000 of their offspring came back—a significant drop from historic average returns of about 760,000 and a 98 percent reduction from 2002. It appeared that Morton's predictions had now come true.

DFO pointed out that salmon farms had been operating in the Broughtons for 20 years and that they could not be responsible for the collapse, because average returns during that time had been trending upward. They produced a bar graph (see sidebar "Pink Salmon Escapement for the Broughton Archipelago") showing pink salmon returns to the Broughtons over the previous 50 years. As well as the record 2001 returns, the graph showed that the 2002 returns were more than double the previous highest return, and the "odd-year" returns had increased since salmon farming was introduced. Five "even-year" returns were lower than the one in 2000, and three of those occurred before salmon farming was introduced to the Broughtons.

Morton responded that during the past eight years, the density of fish stocked at farm sites had quadrupled, giving sea lice many more hosts and much more potential for a population explosion. She cited European studies, which showed that it sometimes took 10 to 15 years after the introduction of salmon farms for lice populations to manifest themselves.

DFO answered that lice reproduce rapidly, with multiple generations per year, and that they are well adapted to exploit new hosts quickly. Therefore, there would be no reason for them to take that long to manifest themselves.

The cause of the collapse will never be known. Morton was convinced that a "wall" of sea lice produced at salmon farms was to blame. DFO stated that it is normal for pink salmon populations to fluctuate over time and that a decline two years after an unusually large return is not unusual.

Because the 2001 run was double the size of any previous run, those fish certainly had less spawning success simply because of the sheer number of them on the spawning beds. Many of the eggs would have been lost as new pairs arrived to spawn in the same patches of gravel—a phenomenon that is well documented elsewhere in B.C. It has also been shown that massive spawning populations can create a higher demand for oxygen than the river can supply and cause further mortalities. Further depletion of dissolved oxygen in a river system can take place when too many eggs and alevins hatch at the same time, and even more fish can be lost.

The millions of juveniles that did make it to the ocean would then have had to compete for food. Only a limited amount of feed—

Male and female Leps
on juvenile chum salmon
collected by Fisheries and
Oceans Canada.

PHOTO Paul Callow/DFO

plankton, in the case of pink and chum—is available in any given area, and when demand outstrips supply, some fish starve. Starving increases stress and weakens fish, leaving them more vulnerable to disease, and slower swimmers are easy targets for parasites such as sea lice. With more hosts, lice populations grow accordingly. This may have been the reason for the distressed, lice-infested fish that Morton sampled with her dipnet. DFO also speculated that natural lice populations were probably higher in 2001 because there was less runoff from a drier winter, therefore higher than average water temperatures and salinity, and lice could reproduce faster.

According to DFO, the high levels of lice Morton reported might also have been the result of the massive pink salmon returns the previous year, which may have generated a huge reservoir of lice that overwintered and reproduced on the outgoing juveniles.

Further DFO research concluded that the 2002 collapse was due to "unidentified events" that took place in the nearshore environment during the spring and early summer of 2001 when fry were outmigrating.

The Pacific Fisheries Resource Conservation Council (PFRCC), an independent body that advises the public and governments on salmon conservation issues, also studied the pink salmon collapse. They found that there was no scientific certainty as to the cause, but that European research had indicated sea-lice abundance may be associated with salmon farming and the decline of wild salmon. They determined that based on current research, combined with the presence of high numbers of sea lice on Broughton salmon and the fact that the pink salmon decline occurred only in that area, sea lice were likely associated with the decline of pinks. The PFRCC recommended that because there was no evidence of some other cause, a coordinated plan to control lice should be undertaken. Either the entire Broughton salmon-farming industry should be fallowed, or it should undertake a combination of fallowing, monitoring and—where lice levels at salmon farms were high—the application of drugs to kill sea lice prior to the spring pink and chum out-migration.

Responding to those recommendations, MAFF formulated the Broughton Archipelago Sea Lice Action Plan in late 2002. Some of the PFRCC's recommendations were implemented, and some of the sites along that corridor were fallowed during the spring of 2003. As well, some farm populations in the area were treated with drugs and others were harvested ahead of schedule.

THE FALLOWING: 2003

In the spring of 2003, DFO intensified its research by using a combination of beach and purse seines and sampled 20,000 juvenile pink and chum salmon in the Broughtons and Knight Inlet, where many of the Broughton pink and chum originate. They found that 25 percent of the fish sampled in the study area were carrying lice, and that those fish had an average of 1.7 lice per infected pink salmon and 2.2 for chum. They found that no fish showed damage caused by lice and no fish appeared to be dying from lice infestation. They concluded that the presence of sea lice on juvenile salmon does not necessarily result in health or growth problems. The study did not address salmon farm–sea lice relationships.

In 2003, Alexandra Morton was also back on the water, surveying pink and chum salmon. In 2001, 2002 and 2003, she had taken samples at three fixed sites adjacent to salmon farms. Salmon were present in those farms during 2001 and 2002. They were fallowed by the spring of 2003 and no salmon were present at the farms during the survey. In 2001, Morton had found 98 percent of the fish at those sites to be carrying lice, with an average of 13.3 lice per fish. In 2002 she found similar results: 92 percent of the fish had lice and the average abundance was 6.8. In 2003, when there were no salmon in the netpens, she found that the number of fish carrying lice dropped dramatically to 36 percent, with an average of 0.64 lice per fish. Because sea-lice

Pink Salmon Escapement for the Broughton Archipelago

This bar graph shows the numbers of pink salmon that were counted by Fisheries and Oceans Canada (DFO) during their annual return to rivers in the Broughtons.

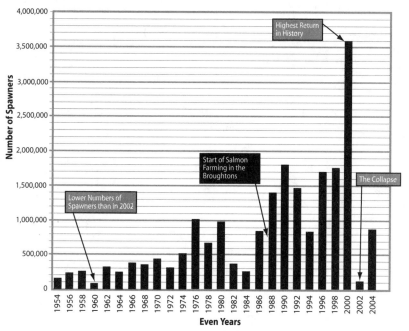

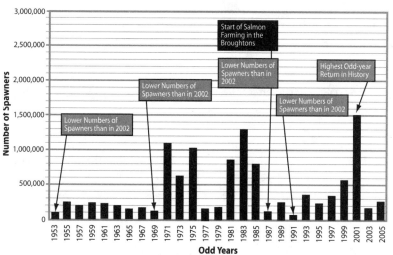

GRAPH Paul Bielicky/Ugly Toad Design

numbers plummeted during the year that no farmed salmon were living nearby, she concluded that salmon farms must have affected the numbers of lice on wild salmon in the vicinity.

The DFO also found low levels of lice in 2003, but they found some of the highest concentrations of lice on wild juvenile salmon in areas where fish farms had been fallowed. DFO speculated that factors other than fallowed salmon farms were responsible for the low levels of lice on the outmigrating pink and chum salmon. Fewer lice may have overwintered as a result of lower returns of salmon in the fall of 2002 and temperatures and salinities were lower throughout the region and therefore less conducive to sea-lice survival compared to 2002. As well, migrating juvenile salmon were larger and healthier in 2003 than in 2002 because there was less competition for food.

In the fall of 2003, returns of pink salmon to the major rivers in the Broughton archipelago—the progeny of the highest ever return of odd-year pink salmon—numbered a disappointing 185,700, down by 87 percent. DFO biologists did not pinpoint a cause, but said that this decline, like the one following the record returns of 2000, was not uncommon two years after a record run and that overspawning and lower food supplies were likely factors.

Historically and recently, chum salmon populations in the Broughtons have not shown the extreme fluctuations exhibited by pink salmon. Because lice affects both species, DFO points out, the relative abundance of the two would parallel each other if sea lice were a primary factor in fish dynamics in the area.

THE RECOVERY: 2004

In 2004, DFO continued its purse- and beach-seine sampling program in the Broughtons. Over 7,000 pink and chum salmon were sampled at 100 sites, and many more lice were found on juvenile pink and chum salmon than during the 2003 survey. Sixty-six percent of the pink salmon sampled had lice—more than double the numbers in 2003—and infected fish had an average of four lice per fish. Sixty-seven percent of the chum sampled had lice, also more than double the number found in 2003. The chum that carried lice had an average of 11 lice per fish. As in 2003, the DFO reported that the infected fish were as healthy as non-infected fish.

In 2003, about half the lice had been Leps and half Caligus. In 2004, Leps were four to five times more predominant than Caligus. No one is certain why that ratio fluctuates—especially when the biomass of farmed salmon is relatively constant in the Broughtons—but DFO said that the changes in species mix and the higher numbers of lice were likely affected by environmental conditions. Water temperatures and salinity were higher than in 2003. Both of those conditions are conducive to higher populations of lice and may affect the species mix as well.

In the fall of 2004, a surprising 895,845 pink salmon returned to the Broughtons. These were the offspring of the "collapsed" 2002 run. The numbers were right in line with average returns over the past 50 years, which indicates that sea lice did not devastate the outmigrating pink and chum salmon, and that pink salmon populations continue to fluctuate greatly from year to year, as they have done for centuries regardless of the presence of salmon farms. However, Alexandra Morton attributed the 2004 escapement rebound to the absence of farmed salmon while the Broughton area was fallowed in 2003. DFO disagreed, because the highest lice infestation rates they saw on migrating pink and chum fry in 2003 were in the fallowed section.

ANOTHER CHAPTER: 2005

At the end of February 2005, Alexandra Morton sampled some of the year's first outmigrating salmon fry. Instead of a dipnet, she used a beach seine in the Burdwood Islands in the central Broughtons. Two sets produced 15 very small pink and chum salmon averaging 0.52 grams (0.02 oz). She found lice on all the fish—an average of four on each—and posted the following message on the Raincoast Research website: "It takes 1 gram of salmon to raise a sea louse; half a gram (0.50) of salmon cannot survive 4 lice. These averages are 8 times the lethal load. If people do not want to see the obvious, I can't help them, but to everyone studying this; the only question is when will the affected wild salmon runs go extinct."

Her sample was small, she acknowledges, but: "I get the same results every season these farms are stocked. Over the next few months this will continue at every stocked farm site in the Broughton

Fisheries and Oceans Canada researchers collect and bag juvenile salmon caught in a beach seine in the Broughtons. The interaction between farmed salmon, sea lice and wild salmon is one of the most controversial issues surrounding the salmon-farming industry.

PHOTO Peter Chettleburgh

and likely coast wide. Next year it will be the same, until there are either no wild salmon or there are no salmon farms in juvenile salmon habitat."

In March 2005, the DFO began its annual purse- and beach-seine sampling program in the Broughtons. They found that 31 percent of the juvenile pink salmon were carrying an average of 1.9 lice per fish, and 33 percent of the chum salmon had an average of three lice per fish. These numbers are very similar to those observed in 2003, when some farms were fallowed, but this time there were more Leps than Caligus. The numbers were lower despite the fact that the farmed salmon biomass in the Broughtons did not change significantly during those two years. As in previous years, the fish that carried lice were reported to be healthy.

DFO scientists are now concluding that as pink and chum salmon populations fluctuate from year to year, sea-lice abundance and species mix also fluctuate, though not necessarily in parallel with salmon. Much more intensive study is needed to learn just how those dynamics work.

Meanwhile, in June 2005, Morton launched a lawsuit against the federal and provincial governments, charging that they were ignoring their own laws in allowing sea lice from salmon farms in the Broughtons to infect wild salmon. In fall 2005, the suit was in the preliminary stages. Morton also predicted another decline in salmon returns to the Broughtons in 2005, and went so far as to say that if she was not correct, she would go back to "the quiet life" of studying killer whales in the area.

In 2005, pink salmon returns to the Broughtons were estimated at 262,701. That number is right in line with average historic returns to the Broughtons. This could mean that even if the presence of salmon farms causes higher levels of lice in the environment, those extra lice are not harming wild salmon populations.

THERE APPEARS TO BE CONSENSUS AMONG CRITICS OF THE INDUSTRY that salmon farms—especially in the Broughtons—are devastating wild salmon runs and will result in their extinction. Unfortunately, only time will tell whether this is true. Government—for whatever reasons—is clearly not prepared to shut down the industry as a precautionary measure.

No one knows what impact sea lice have on various kinds of salmon. What we do know is that populations of pink and, to a lesser extent, chum salmon fluctuate a great deal from year to year, usually with higher returns in even years than in odd years. Research has also shown that sea-lice numbers and the mix of Leps and Caligus vary a great deal from year to year, despite a nearly constant biomass of farmed salmon in the Broughtons. We know that sea lice are more abundant in years of warmer temperatures and lower freshwater runoff from nearby mountains, and less abundant in years with colder temperatures and/or high runoff.

We also know that salmon farms have operated in the Broughtons for 20 years and in the latter years there were record returns of wild salmon to the archipelago. The collapse in 2002 was one of several similar collapses that occurred before the first fish farms opened.

As the sidebar "Abundance of Sea Lice at B.C. Salmon Farms" shows, most salmon that live in the netpens for less than a year have an average of less than one louse per fish. Adult salmon carry as many as six lice per fish in some months and in some areas, including the Broughtons, but in other areas—for example, the west coast of Vancouver Island and the Sunshine Coast—it is rare for adult salmon to have more than two lice each. This compares to an average of

41.5 to 53 lice on wild pink, chum and sockeye salmon returning from offshore waters, as reported in the recent DFO study. We do not know why lice on farmed salmon do not multiply exponentially. The authors of the study published in 2005 in the *Proceedings of the Royal Society of London* found the highest levels of larval lice in the immediate vicinity of salmon farms, yet lice are not reproducing rapidly on farmed salmon. *(or it's being controlled by drugs)*

of course not if you treat them chemically.

As well, we do not know why most of the fish that Alexandra Morton sampled not only had more lice but were dying; whereas in 2003, 2004 and 2005, DFO found that the fish they sampled were healthy, regardless of the presence of lice. The answer may be that the fish Morton sampled had become weak for other reasons and, as a result, became infected with lice, rather than the other way around.

Or the answer may have to do with the different sampling methods. Morton's dipnet system might have captured the portion that was least healthy; and DFO's more random beach- and purse-seine methods may have knocked some of the lice off the fish.

We do know that when salmon farms are infected with lice, higher numbers of lice enter the aquatic environment. But we do not know whether those lice cause more mortalities in juvenile pink and chum salmon—or any salmonid species. So far, DFO's research shows that this is not the case. If research ever does show that the presence of sea lice in salmon farms is affecting juvenile pink and chum salmon populations, significant measures will have to be taken.

Meanwhile, sea-lice abundance will continue to fluctuate from year to year as it has done for eons, according to host availability, salinity and water temperature. Pink salmon populations will also vary significantly year to year, as they have done throughout history.

We know very little about the relationship between sea lice and wild salmonids, except that it is extremely complex. Yet another level of complexity is added when farmed salmon are added to the mix. In the absence of baseline data from the decades before salmon farming, much more research needs to be done if we are to solve any of these mysteries. *copped out again!*

8

DOWN AND DIRTY
Salmon Waste and Farm Pollution

A biologist from Aquametrix Research processes a sediment sample—obtained using a Van Veen grab (clamshell type) sampler—from a salmon-farm site.

PHOTO courtesy Aquametrix Research

FARMED FISH ARE RAISED IN WHAT ARE ESSENTIALLY OCEANIC FEEDLOTS. In British Columbia, the netpens of the 80 or so operating salmon farms occupy a total surface area of about 105 hectares (260 acres). Like all farms, fish farms are artificial additions to the ecosystem and it is important to consider their effect on that ecosystem.

The two primary sources of salmon-farm waste are feces and uneaten feed. Most waste excreted from both wild and farmed salmon is organic, inert, pH-neutral and non-toxic. Fish feed is composed almost entirely of fishmeal, fish oils, vegetable oils, wheat binders and other non-chemical ingredients. Together feces, urine and uneaten feed make up 99 percent of all the waste produced by a salmon farm. The remainder may include antibiotics, chemicals used to control sea lice and traces of copper-based anti-fouling materials applied to nets, walkways and buildings, pathogens shed by fish during disease outbreaks and human waste produced by farm employees.

Because salmon are kept in open cages, uneaten feed and waste are shed directly into the surrounding waters, affecting the makeup of the water column, the bottom sediments below the salmon farm and any marine plants and animals that come into contact with the waste. The buildup of waste under a farm can cause significant changes to the aquatic environment, depending on the size of the salmon farm, the amount of waste produced, the depth of water below the farm, the amount of available oxygen, the bottom topography, local water currents and other factors. All studies undertaken to date by Fisheries and Oceans Canada (DFO) and industry researchers show that the effects of these wastes are localized and temporary. Even at the most poorly sited farms, the sea bottom below the pens begins to revert to its normal state naturally, without intervention or mitigation, as soon as feeding slows or the fish are harvested.

VOLUME OF WASTE

The volume of waste produced by a farm is lowest when smolts are first placed into the netpens. They are physically small and therefore require less feed and produce less waste, though smaller fish actually grow much faster than larger fish. Waste production is highest during summer months that coincide with the point at which salmon are close to their ideal harvest size. This is also when they consume the largest amounts of feed. There are also seasonal fluctuations. For example, salmon do not feed as heavily in winter or when temperatures exceed about 20°C (68°F).

When fish are overfed, more uneaten feed falls to the bottom. Researchers estimate that for every 1,000 grams (35 oz) of feed administered, 30–40 grams (1–1.4 oz) falls through uneaten. Feed is the largest single expense in raising salmon, so it makes economic sense not to waste it. Salmon farmers report that the use of video cameras to monitor and control feeding has reduced the amount of feed that falls through the cages by over 30 percent since the 1980s.

Feed quality has improved as well. Today's feeds are digested more completely and therefore the fish produce less feces. Improved feeds and feeding regimes have reportedly reduced the amount of waste produced annually at an average salmon farm by up to half since the late 1980s.

Stephen Cross, who has been assessing the environmental impacts of salmon aquaculture for the past 18 years, probably knows more than anyone else in B.C. about the effects of salmon farming on the aquatic environment. In 2003 and 2004, he measured sediment buildup under two salmon farms with minimal current flows during an 18-month grow-out cycle. He found that an average of 17 grams (0.6 oz) of waste was deposited per day, per square metre, directly under the netpens at one site, and just over 18 grams (0.65 oz) at the other site (plus or minus about 4 grams/1.5 oz). Using the higher figure, a total of 9.7 kg of waste is deposited per square metre (about

18 lbs/sq yd) during an 18-month growing cycle at a site where current flows do not flush away waste. At sites located among strong currents, there may be no sediment buildup at all.

Anatomy of a Kilogram of Feed

For every kilogram (1,000 grams; 2.2 lbs) of feed:

600–700 g becomes fish meat and energy

70–100 g is "exhaled" through the gills

200–260 g is excreted

30–40 g is uneaten food pellets.

CHART Stolt Sea Farm and Steve Cross

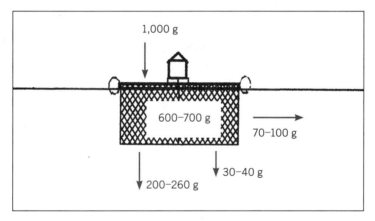

WASTE AND THE WATER COLUMN

Once the uneaten feed and excrement fall through the mesh, they enter the water column. There dissolved organics are dispersed through and around a netpen site and then mixed and diffused by tidal currents. The stronger the current, the quicker and greater the dilution. Studies carried out by both government and industry researchers have shown that most of those organics are assimilated in the water column and undetectable only a few dozen metres from the farm.

In the area adjacent to the farm, some of the nitrates and phosphates that make up the dissolved organics are taken up by aquatic plants and micro-organisms. Farm structures and anchor lines are typically covered in kelp, barnacles and mussels, which in turn support urchins and small fish. Stephen Cross and other researchers have found no evidence that any of the organic material shed from salmon farms is harmful to these organisms, but there is evidence that the added nutrients enhance them. Nutrient enrichment is not always a good thing. For example, extra nutrients in the water can accelerate the growth of certain phytoplankton (microscopic plants) and increase the size and occurrence of algal blooms. However, phytoplankton experts have found that most of the organic nutrients released by a salmon farm are used by organisms in the vicinity of the farm and that statistically insignificant increases in those nutrient concentrations occur downstream from sites, even where there is restricted water exchange. In B.C.'s deep, well-flushed waterways, no link has never been established between salmon farming and the development of harmful phytoplankton blooms, or between salmon farming and general phytoplankton composition, biomass or productivity. To better understand the processes, many salmon farms participate in a joint industry–DFO harmful algae monitoring program.

a double negative?

Manure and Animal Farming

Fifty years ago, most of the manure produced by livestock and poultry in North America was used to enrich the soil. Today, because of the huge concentration of animals in feedlots and confinement buildings, there is no economically feasible way to return the manure to the soil. In Canada alone, the livestock industry produces over 160 billion kilograms (176 million tons) of manure each year. That is more than 14,000 times the amount of waste produced by salmon farms, enough to fill B.C. Place Stadium to the top of the dome 68 times every year—more than once a week. Although livestock and poultry farmers do their best to prevent manure from leeching into the soils and waterways, the sheer volume produced has inevitable consequences.

Manure from warm-blooded animals contains countless organisms, including many types of harmful bacteria, viruses and parasites. These, unlike pathogens from cold-blooded fish, can affect human health. They can find their way into groundwater and be carried by runoff into surface waters. Water contaminated by animal waste causes thousands of bacterial infections in Canada each year. In a single event incident in 2000, 2,300 people were stricken by gastroenteritis and 6 people died in Walkerton, Ontario, as a direct result of contamination when their drinking water was contaminated by E. coli bacteria from livestock manure.

THE OXYGEN QUESTION

Oxygen is an essential component of sea water, and most of the plants and organisms on land as well as in the aquatic environment need oxygen for their basic life processes. Salmon take dissolved oxygen from the water through their gills and produce carbon dioxide. In a salmon farm, high densities of fish have a high demand for oxygen. Salmon are known to be more sensitive to depressed oxygen levels than most other species. As long as tidal currents are constantly flushing water through a salmon farm, the fish have a constant supply of oxygenated water. When there are no such currents, the salmon are the first species to sicken and die. Therefore, it is in the best interests of the salmon farmer to place pens so that currents are continually flushing them. That is why salmon farming has been shown not to consume enough of the available oxygen to harm other organisms.

Deep water in B.C. is very low in oxygen because of global water circulation patterns. Our deep water has been out of the light for hundreds of years when currents cause it to upwell (rise into shallower waters) off the coast. This natural upwelling of deep water is the major source of low-oxygen water in the area, but this deep water also contributes to the naturally high productivity in the Pacific Northwest because it is very high in nutrients.

WASTE AND THE SEABED

The majority of the organic wastes produced by salmon farming do not persist in the water column. They are denser than the surrounding water and therefore fall to the sea floor. Where they land and how they accumulate depends on the depth, tidal currents and quantity discharged. According to Stephen Cross, while the average salmon farm produces just under 10 kilograms per square metre of waste (18 lbs/sq yd) per year, averaged over a two-year grow-out cycle, not all that waste ends up settling to the ocean floor. The deeper the water and the faster the current, the more widely the sediments are dispersed, and the more efficiently the bacteria and organisms on the sea floor can assimilate them.

Currents also provide a steady supply of oxygenated water over the sea floor. Oxygen is vital to the bacteria and other sea-bottom organisms that help to break down organic waste. At a good site, water flows constantly over the sediments, replenishing oxygen and keeping the organisms working. But there are physical limits at the upper end. Too much current makes it more difficult to raise salmon because it puts more strain on nets and anchor lines. As well, a flow of more than about 3 or 4 knots would contribute to stressing the fish.

Many early salmon farms in B.C. were sited at depths of 35 metres (115 ft) or less, in areas that did not have adequate currents. Today in B.C., sites at depths of 45–70 metres (150–230 ft) are the norm, and some are as deep as 150 metres (500 ft). At the best sites, depth and current combine to scour the ocean floor continuously so that there is no sediment buildup, even at peak production. This is the exception, not the rule: most salmon farms in B.C. have some amount of waste buildup.

Both DFO and industry studies have shown that almost all of the sediment that does build up around a salmon farm accumulates directly below the netpens and outward from the perimeter by 5–10 metres (16–33 ft). A small amount of secondary sedimentation occurs to 30–50 metres (100–165 ft) from the perimeter. Beyond that point, sedimentation is either non-existent or barely detectable. During peak summer feeding times, waste buildup can sometimes be detected as far as 145–200 metres (475–650 ft) from the netcages. (Salmon farms typically array their anchors 250–300 metres (820–984 ft) out from the netcages.)

Those sediments can settle on a variety of bottom types. Some are flat and muddy or sandy; others are steeper and lined with rock, gravel or cobbles. Muddy bottoms are typical of slow current flows from which natural sediments have dropped out and built up over thousands of years. Sand, rock, gravel and cobble bottoms are typical of steeper slopes and faster currents, where sedimentation has been minimal.

ASSIMILATION OF WASTE
With or without salmon farms, many types of bacteria, worms, small shrimp-like crustaceans, sea stars, sea cucumbers, crab and small shellfish dwell on the sea floor and feed on organic sediments. Worms are essential in this process because they are constantly turning the sediments over, which helps the bacteria to break them down.

Natural chemicals and the oxygen in sea water also aid in assimilating organics. Little plant life occurs below salmon farms because farms are generally situated in water deeper than 45–50 metres (150–165 ft), where light-dependent plants such as algae and seaweed cannot dominate.

If the salmon farm does not shed waste faster than these organisms can assimilate it, the waste has little or no negative impact on the organisms' natural background levels or the chemistry of the bottom. But if waste accumulates faster than the site can assimilate it, much more pronounced changes can take place.

When sedimentation rates are low and currents are good, the bacteria and other organisms very close to the salmon farm may become more abundant and diverse because of added nutrients from the salmon-farm waste. The site can in turn become more efficient at assimilating waste.

In general, when the rate of sedimentation is in balance with the ability of the site to assimilate those wastes, the site is said to be in an aerobic, or oxygen-based, state. When sedimentation increases beyond this balance point, organic material collects faster than it can be assimilated. The bacteria need more oxygen to keep up. When the demand of oxygen exceeds the supply, oxygen-dependent organisms are displaced by those more tolerant of a low-oxygen environment, and the abundance and diversity of bacteria and animal life begins to change. In extreme conditions, virtually all the aerobic bacteria and organisms can be smothered. When this happens, the aquatic life of the sediment moves from aerobic to anaerobic (oxygen-free).

Anaerobic conditions favour species of bacteria that use sulphur instead of oxygen in breaking down matter. A large, patchy white mat of sulphide-oxidizing bacteria is often associated with these conditions. The by-products of anaerobic decomposition include methane and sulphur compounds such as sulphur dioxide and hydrogen sulphide. Researchers have found that most of these gases remain in the sediment layers, and if they build up enough to be released into the water column, they are reduced or assimilated by oxidization, diffusion and mixing as they rise.

In areas where salmon farming does not take place, anaerobic conditions are often present when currents are low and/or bays or

This is what is occurring — and the marine life is a very serious condition is not occurring? And author this very negative impact [handwritten margin notes]

lagoons have minimal tidal exchange. These conditions limit the amount of available oxygen. In the vicinity of salmon farms, organic loading is much higher than would occur in the wild, and anaerobic conditions can develop in areas where it would not normally occur. In the 1980s, little was known about the effects that salmon farms would have on the ocean floor. Sites were chosen not for their ability to grow healthy fish or to cause minimal damage to the bottom, but for their closeness to market, shelter from weather and shallow waters that made for easier anchoring. The sea floor under some those sites had almost continuous anaerobic conditions.

Today, with stronger anchoring systems, sturdier netpen construction and more information on environmental impact, salmon farmers locate their farms at deeper and less protected sites. Gradually the older, poorly sited salmon farms—which represent about 20 percent of the tenures—are being moved to sites where tidal currents ensure the constant exchange of oxygen-rich water over the bottom and anaerobic conditions are less likely to occur.

However, when anaerobic conditions do occur, they are not permanent. After waste loading is reduced to the point where oxygen-dependent bacteria and organisms can thrive, they reclaim the site and aerobic conditions return. This process occurs without human intervention, and numerous studies have shown that depending on the site and the degree of anaerobic conditions, recovery can take place within a few weeks, or as long as four years for the most poorly located sites.

DRUGS, CHEMICALS AND THE AQUATIC ENVIRONMENT

The 1 percent of salmon-farm waste that is not organic material can include antibiotics, sea-lice treatment and/or other chemicals.

In 2005, Stephen Cross completed a three-year study (funded by DFO and the National Research Council) in which he hung an array of shellfish in baskets at two salmon farms for the duration of their Atlantic and chinook salmon grow-out cycles. One farm was in an area of minimal current (slow site), the other in an area of strong currents (fast site). Cross chose shellfish because they are known to accumulate even the most minute concentrations of pollutants in their tissues and are therefore very good sentinels. At each farm,

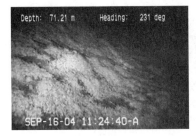

Depth: 71.21 m   Heading: 231 deg

SEP-16-04 11:24:40-A

Depth: 49.88 m   Heading: 58 deg

SEP-16-04 11:45:57-A

Polychaete worms are considered opportunistic species. They proliferate in areas where organic enrichment occurs because they are better able than other worms to withstand the physical buildup of such organic loads and the associated changes in oxygen level.

PHOTO courtesy Aquametrix Research

The appearance of the natural sea floor (not associated with a salmon farm) at depths below the region influenced by light. The surface of these sediments is often inhabited by animals that live on (and not within) the substrate, such as shrimp, crab and brittle stars (shown here).

PHOTO courtesy Aquametrix Research

Depth: 64.36 m   Heading: 262 deg

Depth: 104.56 m   Heading: 84 deg

MAR- 4-04 10:04:50-A

The appearance of the natural sea floor at depths greater than 50 metres (165 ft). Limited light prevents the kelp forest situation typical in shallower marine areas. The dominant organisms in these soft-bottom environmwents live within the substrate and thus are not readily seen at the surface.

PHOTO courtesy Aquametrix Research

A bacterial layer (*Beggiatoa* sp.) sometimes develops over the top of freshly deposited organic material. At sites where organic material is readily assimilated into the environment, the net accumulation of organics may result in a light, typically patchy "dusting" of these bacteria over the sea floor.

PHOTO courtesy Aquametrix Research

Depth: 94.51 m   Heading: 88 deg

MAR- 4-04 10:06:43-A

In areas of heavy organic loading, which can occur under log-booming grounds or directly under fish farms at sites with low tidal flow, the prevalence of *Beggiatoa* is high and the seabed surface is seen with dense white mats (the bacteria) overlaying black, anoxic sediments.

PHOTO courtesy Aquametrix Research

baskets were placed inside the netpen, at the edge of the pen, at points 10–225 metres (33–750 ft) from the pen and at various locations from top to bottom of the water column. The shellfish were sampled for pollutants a number of times during the production cycle. Cross tested for residues of antibiotics, sea-lice drugs and a suite of trace metals, including copper and zinc. His findings mirror those of other such research projects—that there are traces of these compounds in the immediate vicinity of salmon farms.

ANTI-FOULING TREATMENTS

The copper-based anti-fouling treatments that many salmon farmers apply to nets and farm structures are toxic: they stop the buildup of algae, seaweeds, barnacles, mussels and other organisms by poisoning them.

In the early 1980s, a tin-based paint, tributyltin (TBT) was used for this purpose, but the B.C. Salmon Farmers Association banned its use in 1985 after research demonstrated that the paint was damaging shellfish. It has been banned for most North American pleasure craft since 1989 for the same reason, but it is still available for use on large commercial vessels worldwide.

The standard product used today on B.C. salmon farms is latex-based Flexigard, which contains 26.5 percent cuprous-oxide—about half the concentration of copper in standard anti-fouling paints used on boat bottoms. Flexigard is specially formulated for use on salmon-farm nets. The nets are dipped in the paint at facilities on shore and allowed to dry in the open air.

All anti-fouling treatments must be approved for use by the Canadian government, and according to Health Canada and the

Canadian Food Inspection Agency (CFIA), no health risks are associated with copper in fish. Humans are exposed to proportionally higher levels of copper every day by handling pennies and drinking water from copper pipes, with no ill effects. Stephen Cross's study found that even in shellfish whose cages were inches from a freshly treated net, only minute traces of copper had accumulated. Elevated levels of copper have been found in sediments, though recent mandatory monitoring at all salmon farms has shown no copper at all, or traces of copper within the limits considered safe by government. As well, the CFIA tests for copper in salmon at fish-processing plants. Copper has never been shown to accumulate in the flesh of farmed salmon.

Despite the apparently low environmental risk of using antifouling paint on nets, about 20 percent of salmon farms choose not to treat their nets, but to pressure-wash them in place as required during the grow-out cycle.

TRACE METALS

Trace amounts of metals are present in sea water and in every marine organism. They occur naturally and are necessary for proper brain functioning in both wild and farmed fish. For farmed salmon, the essential minerals—most notably zinc—are incorporated into feed. Stephen Cross and other researchers have found slightly elevated levels of zinc in the water column and in sediments 10–30 metres (33–100 ft) from the netpens and directly below them. However, zinc is assimilated over time, and Cross found no zinc accumulation in any of the shellfish he studied over the three years. According to provincial regulations, all salmon farms must test for zinc in sediments on a regular basis.

SHELLFISH CONTAMINATION

Stephen Cross's study was designed in part to address public concerns about the potential contamination of shellfish beds by salmon farm pollution. He placed the baskets of shellfish directly downstream of the main current flow through the test farms, to ensure that the shellfish intercepted any waterborne contamination from the farm sites. Over the three years, Cross found none of the pollutants related to salmon farms farther than 150 metres (330 ft) from the perimeter of a salmon farm. B.C. law prohibits salmon farms from operating within 300 metres (1,000 ft) of a recognized shellfish bed, so Cross concluded that salmon farming was unlikely to harm shellfish.

HUMAN SEWAGE

Another pollutant associated with salmon farming is the human sewage produced by staff who live on salmon farms. Unlike fish waste, human sewage contains harmful E. coli bacteria that can be transmitted to other humans and cause illness. The Ministry of Agriculture and Lands' Finfish Aquaculture Waste Regulations require that salmon farms install septic tanks (with a minimum retention time of two days) or other devices that ensure total suspended solids do not exceed 130 milligrams per litre (0.02 oz/gal). The discharge point for effluent must be at least 15 metres (50 ft) below the surface. No sludge discharge is permitted, and holding tanks are pumped out as required and hauled away.

FARM WASTE AND WILD FISH

Because other fish use the waters around salmon farms, salmon-farm pollution could be harming wild fish. As part of mandatory sea-floor monitoring programs, Stephen Cross regularly uses a remotely operated vehicle to videotape aquatic activity around and under salmon farms. He reports that he does see prawns and the occasional crab, ratfish or flatfish under farms, but his surveys have not found fish populations living under salmon farms. This is to be expected— federal and provincial siting regulations do not allow salmon farms to be located in any area that is productive fish habitat, such as reefs or halibut holes. As well, wild salmon do not live in association with salmon farms. They may pass by the farms as juveniles on their seaward migration and as adults returning to spawn, but they do not stay in the area long enough to be affected by salmon farm pollution. Just as wild salmon avoid plankton blooms, they can also avoid any areas where they don't like the smell or water chemistry.

REGULATING THE IMPACTS

The best way to avoid waste buildup and anaerobic conditions is to establish a farm in the right place. The industry continues to move in this direction for its own reasons, but the B.C. government has introduced regulations to ensure that fish-farm waste does not create long-term anaerobic conditions or damage ecosystem components. The Finfish Aquaculture Waste Regulations, introduced in 2003, established thresholds of solid-waste accumulation on the sea floor. Salmon farmers must monitor the sediments under each farm before stocking and during peak production. This monitoring may be undertaken by the farm companies themselves, or by independent consultants such as Cross. Either way, provincial authorities audit the process and the findings. A salmon farm may not be restocked if sediment levels exceed the threshold. The assessment is made by measuring what are known as micromoles of total sulphides. The level of sulphides in the sediment indicates whether the chemical change associated with the shift from aerobic to anaerobic conditions is taking place. During peak production, total sulphides cannot exceed 6,000 micromoles—the point at which aerobic conditions give way to anaerobic conditions and the species composition starts to change. Once the fish are harvested, the farm may not be restocked until the sulphide level drops to 1,350 micromoles. At this level, there might be slightly higher than normal organic loads, but the sea floor is fully aerobic and the sediments are enriching the organisms, not displacing them.

Not everyone agrees that the sulphide-measuring process is effective or that the established "safe" levels are actually safe. Levings et al. studied the question in 2002 and concluded that the standards did not appear to be sufficient to prevent the loss of productive capacity of bottom sediments. They determined that adverse effects on the benthic community can occur at concentrations well below the 1,300 micromole standard. They cite other research showing that levels of 1,000 micromoles can reduce the diversity of sediment-dwelling macroinvertebrates by 50 percent. Major changes to benthic life take place closer to the 6,000 micromole level, but more study is needed to determine the effects of smaller changes in bottom sediments.

The practice of fallowing salmon farms for several months after harvest to eliminate any leftover pathogens has the effect of allowing the sediment to recover its balance naturally. (but only down to 1350)

Waste in the Waterways

Our oceans, lakes and rivers have been used as garbage dumps—legally and illegally—for human, agricultural and industrial waste for thousands of years.

The B.C. forest industry holds tenure to almost 19,000 hectares (47,500 acres) of marine log-storage grounds. As any boater knows, hundreds of log booms are stored in sheltered bays throughout the coast at any given time. The logs shed bark as they chafe in the booms, and this bark has been building up and smothering bottom sediments for decades. The arthropods and crustaceans that are a normal part of sediment biology have disappeared. Bark does not break down easily, so we can expect the effects of it to remain for decades after the logs are gone.

The Fraser River drains most of B.C. and is home to most of its human population. The river has had to absorb much of the waste from our agricultural and industrial activity over many decades. We have released hundreds of toxins into this river, in which millions of salmon must travel to reach their spawning grounds and the sea.

Canada spreads about 34 million kilograms (37,400 tons) of pesticides annually over 35 million hectares (87.5 million acres). It distributes about 3 billion tonnes (2.7 billion tons) of commercial fertilizers over 24 million hectares (60 million acres). The Canadian livestock industry produces more than 160 billion kilograms (176 million tons) of manure each year. All of these compounds find their way into the land, waterways or oceans.

Each summer, a continuing series of algal blooms results from the massive amounts of nitrogen and phosphorus carried down the Mississippi River and into the Gulf. This zone—an area three-quarters of the size of Vancouver Island—is devoid of fish and shrimp, which once supported a significant commercial fishery. Dead zones have been reported in at least 50 other coastal regions around the world—including Chesapeake Bay on the east coast of the U.S. In contrast, nutrients released from salmon farms are said to have a statistically insignificant impact on the aquatic environment.

As a result of pesticides, fertilizers and other industrial compounds used on land, it is almost impossible to find fish—or humans—anywhere in the world whose bodies are free of toxic chemicals. Uncontaminated fish and other animal products may simply no longer exist.

The tone of this little essay proves that author is rationalizing his defense of salmon farming — does he mean that the contamination is acceptable "because" everybody does it"?

EXPERIENCE HAS SHOWN US THAT IT IS A GOOD IDEA TO ASSUME THAT any manufactured chemical and any concentrated farm waste is harmful to the environment until proven otherwise, and that government and industry cannot always be relied on to act in the best interests of the natural environment. The salmon-farming industry is still in its infancy, so if we are vigilant, we have the opportunity to prevent the damage that chemicals and waste from land-based farming have done to both the land and aquatic environment.

9

MAKING A SWIM FOR IT

Escapes

An Atlantic Salmon Watch Program crew member surveys a creek for escaped Atlantic salmon.

PHOTO courtesy *Northern Aquaculture*

SINCE THE MID-1980S, ABOUT 1.5 MILLION FISH HAVE ESCAPED FROM British Columbia salmon farms: 500,000 Atlantic salmon, 1 million chinook and 13,000 coho salmon. In the Puget Sound area of Washington State, over 600,000 Atlantic salmon have escaped since 1990. These numbers, which are based on reported escapes only, probably represent minimums. Not only do escapes cause financial losses, they generate bad publicity for salmon farmers.

In the early years of salmon farming in B.C., fish escaped because of poorly sited farms that broke apart in storms, predators that chewed holes in nets, and nets cut by propellers when boats were handled poorly. Over time, as anchoring systems improved, regulations stipulated the use of stronger nets, almost all farmers installed predator control nets, and fish-handling and net-maintenance procedures got better, the number of escapes has been reduced.

As well, every salmon farm in B.C. must have in place a government-approved escape prevention plan and an escape response plan. Staff must be trained to know how to respond appropriately to escapes and efforts must be made to recover any escaped fish.

The success of these measures can be seen in the average number of annual escapes from salmon farms compared to the number of fish being raised in netpens—typically about 20 million. As shown in the sidebar "Reported Escapes of Farmed Salmon in B.C.," numbers are declining steadily. For example, B.C.'s farmed-salmon production tripled between 1990 and 1999, but escapes remained stable at about 1 percent of production, or about 50,000 fish per year. Between 2000 and 2005, escapes averaged just under 30,000. In nearby Washington State, there have been no reported escapes since 1999.

[handwritten margin notes: Yes, we do — Now way look at ENO where are salmon now almost extinct]

We do not know what impact escaped salmon—particularly non-indigenous species such as Atlantic salmon—have on wild salmon stocks. Atlantic salmon represent about 80 percent of the farmed salmon raised in B.C. Concerns have been raised that escaped Atlantic salmon will take over spawning streams and displace native Pacific salmon, that farmed Pacific salmon will interbreed with wild stocks and degrade the genetic pool, that escaped farmed fish will transfer disease to wild fish and that they will rob wild fish of food, spawning and rearing habitat.

It is difficult to quantify these effects, because we do not know how many fish escape, where they go or how well they survive.

[handwritten note: But you just gave figures on number of escapees!]

TRACKING 'EM DOWN

Pacific salmon represent 15–25 percent of the farmed-salmon production in B.C. Because farmed Pacific salmon are physically identical to wild Pacific salmon (though farmed salmon may show wear on their fins from being confined to netpens), they are not easily identified as escaped farmed salmon when they are encountered in the wild. Our only source of information on Pacific salmon is reports by salmon farms.

For non-native Atlantic salmon, which differ from Pacific salmon in coloration and markings, escape reporting is just one source of information. The Atlantic Salmon Watch Program (ASWP) was established in 1991 by Fisheries and Oceans Canada (DFO) and the provincial Ministry of Agriculture, Food and Fisheries (now the Ministry of Agriculture and Lands, or MAL) to provide a central database for Atlantic salmon escapes and recaptures. The ASWP also operates a river-sampling program. Crews of divers survey rivers and streams looking for adult Atlantic salmon (which can spawn) and juveniles (which can result from spawning). That information is supplemented by data collected in the saltwater environment from commercial, sport and Native fishermen, freshwater-stream surveys by provincial and DFO stock-assessment crews, and poster campaigns, direct mail and phone calls.

Reported Escapes of Farmed Salmon in B.C.

YEAR	MARINE ATLANTIC SALMON	FRESHWATER ATLANTIC SALMON	TOTAL ATLANTIC	CHINOOK SALMON	COHO SALMON	TOTAL ESCAPES
1987				22,422		22,422
1988				2,000		2,000
1989				392,271		392,271
1990				165,000		165,000
1991	6,651		6,651	229,500		242,802
1992	9,544		9,544	59,632		69,176
1993	11,500		11,500		12,113	23,613
1994	63,929	7,000	70,929	2,300		73,229
1995	51,883	941	52,824	5,000	1,000	58,824
1996	13,104	40,000	53,104			53,104
1997	7,471	10,464	17,935	38,956		56,891
1998	88,968	300	89,268	1,900		91,168
1999	35,730		35,730			35,730
2000	37,392		37,392	31,555		40,547
2001	57,643	247	57,890	78		57,968
2002	9,282		9,282	9,098	100	18,480
2003	34		34	2	1	37
2004	43,969		43,969	5	11	43,985
2005*	6		6	1	41	47
Total	437,106	58,952	496,058	959,720	13,266	1,469,044

* To December 2005
SOURCE: ATLANTIC SALMON WATCH PROGRAM

Workers survey a creek for juvenile Atlantic salmon, using an electro-shocking device.

PHOTO Steve Schut

The effectiveness of these measures is restricted by the difficulty in locating escaped salmon at sea, the fact that not all fishermen know the difference between Atlantic and Pacific salmon, and limited ASWP budgets that allow surveys in only a small number of the rivers. One report suggests that on Vancouver Island alone, only about 1 percent of the potential rearing habitat was being monitored in 2005. The same can be said for virtually all fisheries- and wildlife-assessment programs: all fish and wildlife populations are hard to monitor. The accuracy of the ASWP stream surveys is further limited by the area of the stream surveyed, the visibility and the time of year.

Once more than about half a dozen Atlantic salmon are identified in a stream, DFO and ASWP staff attempt to destroy the fish. Adults are generally removed by spear-fishing and fry are removed by dipnets and hand lures.

Efforts have also been made to recover escaped fish in salt water with commercial fishing gear, but it is impossible to determine the recovery rate accurately. About 19,000 Atlantic salmon have been caught in commercial and sport fisheries in salt water since 1987, most of them in Johnstone Strait and Queen Charlotte Sound in gillnet fisheries. We do not know how many have been captured but not reported.

SURVIVAL IN THE WILD

Escaped Atlantic salmon have been found in freshwater rivers and streams as far north as Alaska, so it is clear that they can survive in the wild. The question is: how many survive? Again, because of the difficulty in identifying escaped Pacific salmon, most of the data we have is based on Atlantic salmon. One exception is information gathered in 1994 and 1995, when DFO scientists Henrick Kreiberg and W. Craig Clarke released, at different times of the year, almost 47,000 chinook salmon of various weights up to 441 grams (15 oz) raised at DFO's experimental salmon farm in Nanaimo. The study was designed to simulate escapes from commercial salmon farms and to determine whether the fish would survive and where they would end up. Only 19 of the tagged fish were ever recovered, 16 in Vancouver Island waters north of Nanaimo and 3 farther south, including Puget Sound. Kreiberg and Clarke found no significant difference in recovery rates for different sizes or seasons of release.

It is possible that Atlantic salmon are not suited for life in the wild in this area. More than 200 attempts have been made to introduce Atlantic salmon into B.C. waters to enhance sport fishing (see sidebar "Before There Were Pacifics, There Were Atlantics"), and all have failed.

As well, only a tiny percentage of escaped Atlantic salmon have been observed in fresh water. Approximately 500,000 Atlantic salmon have escaped since 1985—and these are just the reported escapes. Of those, 1,091 adults were seen in fresh water.

In 1997, 370,000 farmed Atlantic salmon escaped from Puget Sound in Washington State. It was the largest escape incident ever recorded on the West Coast. Regular commercial salmon fisheries were taking place in the area at the time, and fishermen captured 2,200 of the escaped fish. Later, at 16 rivers with fish-counting fences, a total of 53 salmon were recovered. It is likely that the rest of them starved or were eaten by predators. or not —

203

Any farmed fish that escapes will perish unless it learns to forage in the wild. Scientists do not know whether fish brought up on a steady supply of pellets can develop the foraging skills of their wild counterparts.

Farmed salmon show a distinct lack of predatory behaviour toward wild prey, such as herring and perch that occasionally wander in through the mesh of netpens. Some of these visitors feed on pellets with the salmon and grow to a size that prevents them from leaving the netpens. Farm staff who monitor feeding with underwater cameras report that they often see small fish—natural prey of salmon—swimming unmolested among the farm population.

ASWP studies of the stomach contents of recaptured escaped Atlantic salmon over 10 years consistently show that 95 percent of Atlantic salmon recovered in B.C. have no prey in their stomachs. Salmon recovered in Alaska—a long way to go without feeding—don't fare much better: 93 percent of them have empty stomachs. Atlantic salmon have a high proportion of body fat that could sustain them for some time. That may explain how these escaped fish survived—a speculation that is supported by the reduced fat content of those fish captured in Alaska. Comparative studies on wild coho and chinook salmon show that 75–80 percent of them have prey items in their stomachs.

which may explain the difference in texture

Another factor in the survival of escaped fish is predators. Wild fish must evade predators from the moment they hatch, but farmed Atlantics rarely even see predators and may not have the skills to avoid them. As well, since they apparently do not learn to forage, they eventually become weaker and even more prone to predation. Farmed salmon are selected for traits such as docile behaviour, which makes them easier to raise in a farm environment. This too can make escaped farmed salmon easier prey, especially for mammals such as river otters and seals.

Before There Were Pacifics, There Were Atlantics

Prior to the evolution of Pacific salmon, Atlantic salmon (*Salmo salar*) were widespread throughout the northern hemisphere, including the north Pacific Ocean. Some 15 million years ago, the Pacific salmonids (genus *Oncorhynchus*) evolved and Atlantic salmon became extinct in Pacific waters, either because the genus could not adapt to the changing environment or because Pacific salmon were more successful in competing for food or on spawning beds.

In the early years of the 20th century, fisheries managers tried to reintroduce Atlantic salmon to the Pacific Ocean to enhance sport fishing opportunities with this "prize" fish. Between 1905 and 1935, nearly 200 introductions of 8.6 million Atlantic salmon—as eggs, alevins, fry or smolts—were made into 60 different lakes and rivers and streams along the coast of B.C. Nine other countries outside the native range of Atlantic salmon have also tried to introduce Atlantic salmon into coastal waters. All have failed. (Coho and chinook salmon, however, were so successfully introduced into the Great Lakes that they are now outdoing Atlantic salmon and hampering restocking efforts.)

There are differences, however, between those attempts to introduce Atlantic salmon and the potential impact of farmed Atlantics. To introduce them, eggs or juvenile salmon were transplanted. They had to survive at sea and compete for food against many more wild fish than there are now, and then, after several years, return to spawn. In contrast, about half the fish that escape from salmon farms are adults and do not have to survive as long to mature sexually. Another difference is that today's farmed Atlantic salmon are the result of many generations of parents raised in the Pacific Ocean, and they may be more acclimatized to local conditions. These changes may not be significant enough to give Atlantic salmon any better odds for survival. Even in a stock's native range, once it has become extinct, it is extremely difficult to re-establish.

ESCAPE ROUTES

Salmon that escape from farms are thought to spend some time in the vicinity of their netpens, then gradually disperse. Some mature fish make their way to nearby rivers and streams, where, if they can survive to sexual maturity and find mates of the same species, they may spawn.

We know that escaped salmon can travel great distances. Since 1990, two escaped Atlantic salmon (thought to have originated in B.C.) have been caught in the Bering Sea (about 2,000 kilometres /1,200 mi away) and just under 600 Atlantics (again, likely from B.C. farms) have been caught in Alaskan waters.

We also know that some escapees ascend rivers and streams and attempt to spawn. Since data was first collected, adult Atlantic salmon have been found in 81 of B.C.'s 3,150 wild salmon-producing rivers and streams—mainly on Vancouver Island, but escapees have also been found in the Fraser River and its tributaries, Burrard Inlet and Howe Sound, a few other coastal rivers and as far north as Alaska. Wild salmon return to their birth streams, possibly because they are imprinted with the smell of their home streams during their out-migration and then use their sense of smell to find their way back. We do not know how or why escaped farmed salmon choose rivers. If salmon navigate by smell, we could assume that an escaped farmed fish would go back to its hatchery creek. Scientists believe that the imprinting of wild fish also involves remembering the route they followed from the birth stream to the open ocean. Farmed salmon don't have that learned information.

Where Have All the Wild Atlantics Gone?

In their native habitat, Atlantic salmon spawn from fall through spring and then spend up to three years in fresh water. They then migrate to sea and spend up to three more years there before they return to fresh water to spawn. Unlike Pacific salmon (except steelhead), which die after spawning, Atlantic salmon may spawn several times.

Scientists have estimated that at one time more than 10 million Atlantic salmon returned annually to spawn in streams draining into the north Atlantic, from New York to Portugal. These are not high numbers when compared to wild Pacific salmon on the west coast. In B.C., historic annual returns of sockeye (as well as pink salmon) to the Fraser River alone often exceeded that number.

Fishing and development almost completely extinguished Atlantic salmon from Canada's Great Lakes in the late 1800s. Atlantic salmon are also extinct in southern Europe. Salmon farming is often blamed for the demise of Atlantic salmon, but wild populations throughout their range have been declining for more than 50 years, mostly because of overfishing and habitat destruction. The decline began well before salmon farming started. But in areas where farmed Atlantic salmon outnumber wild Atlantic salmon at ratios of about 100:1, few would argue that they are having a positive effect on wild stocks.

Escaped Atlantic salmon that have never migrated may simply home in on the smell of fresh water. There is some evidence that if escaped salmon make it to fresh water, they tend to enter streams near to where they escaped. For example, in DFO Management Area 12, which includes the Broughtons—the site of the highest concentration of salmon farms in B.C.—177 adult Atlantics were found in 15 rivers throughout that area. Of those fish, for some reason almost a third were observed in a single river system (Adam/Eve) in Johnstone Strait.

Freshwater Adult Atlantic Salmon Sightings and Captures

YEAR	NUMBER OF SIGHTINGS	NUMBER OF RIVERS
1987	1	1
1988	0	0
1989	0	0
1990	3	1
1991	8	5
1992	48	9
1993	23	12
1994	50	11
1995	57	19
1996	211	30
1997	129	30
1998	90	28
1999	184	14
2000	131	18
2001	116	13
2002	40	14
*2003	36	N/A
*2004	0	0
*2005	2	1

* Incomplete data set/limited surveys
SOURCE: ATLANTIC SALMON WATCH PROGRAM

SPAWNING IN THE WILD

Before Atlantic salmon were introduced in B.C. for aquaculture, DFO told the public that if any fish did manage to escape from salmon farms, they would not be able to spawn and therefore would not pose a threat to native populations. We now know that is not true.

Between 1998—when Atlantic salmon were first found spawning in fresh water in B.C.—and 2003, 405 juvenile salmon have either been sighted or captured in nine streams and three lakes. More than half of those (243) are believed to be escapees from freshwater enhancement facilities, including 191 from two freshwater lakes with netpen rearing facilities. The balance were likely the offspring of successful spawning.

We know that escaped farmed fish can spawn in the wild (though Atlantic salmon do not breed with Pacific salmon), but DFO believes that they produce many less viable offspring than their wild counterparts. Atlantic salmon can spawn later, earlier or at the same time as Pacific salmon. If they were to spawn at the same time, farmed fish could compete with wild fish for prime spawning areas, then defend them against wild fish attempting to spawn in that patch of gravel. They could also inadvertently dig up eggs laid by wild Pacific salmon.

However, a 2001 study by the University of Guelph, on Pacific–Atlantic interactions on spawning beds in Lake Ontario, where Pacific salmon were introduced in the early 1900s to rebuild depleted wild Atlantic salmon stocks, showed clearly that coho and chinook competed successfully against wild Atlantic salmon in their native range. This indicates that native Pacific salmon are likely to outdo escaped Atlantics on the west coast.

Sterile Salmon?

One way to ensure that escaped farmed salmon do not reproduce in the wild is to sterilize all farmed salmon. Research so far has included producing triploid fish, which contain an extra chromosome. Instead of being xx or xy, the fish may be xxx or xxy. The methods used to produce triploid fish include applying stress using high pressure, high temperature, cold and/or chemicals to the eggs at a specific point after they are fertilized. The shock causes an extra set of chromosomes to be produced, making the fish viable but sterile.

To salmon farmers the advantage of such a process is that fish would not expend their energy in becoming sexually mature and would therefore grow faster. But so far, the method is not 100 percent effective: fish have not been shown to grow larger, and they are often more prone to disease. As well, the process has not been developed on a large enough scale for commercial salmon farming.

When wild Pacific salmon spawn, a female lays about 3,000 eggs, usually over a period of several hours. On average, about 10 percent survive to the fry stage. In contrast, an Atlantic salmon lays from 10,000 to 14,000 eggs, though they are much smaller. Studies in B.C. have shown that fertility of farmed salmon, both Atlantic and Pacific females, is significantly lower than that of wild salmon. A Norwegian study showed that farmed Atlantic females were only 20–40 percent as successful at spawning as wild females, and that farmed Atlantic males were less than 3 percent as successful as wild Atlantic males in spawning performance. Therefore, although escaped salmon can spawn in fresh water in B.C., they are much less likely than their wild counterparts to produce healthy offspring.

In his 2001 publication *Super un-Natural: Atlantic Salmon in B.C. Waters*, Dr. John Volpe summarized his research into Atlantic salmon spawning behaviour. He constructed a spawning channel designed for Atlantic salmon on the Little Qualicum River on Vancouver Island, then stocked it with mature Atlantic salmon and observed their spawning behaviour. Volpe demonstrated that Atlantic salmon could successfully spawn and produce viable offspring in the simulated natural environment, but, as in the Norwegian study, reproductive success was low. He found that most females matured sexually but did not spawn, and that the females that did spawn retained many of their eggs, built poor redds and produced less viable eggs. Volpe also found that most of the males matured, but were much more subdued in their spawning behaviour than wild Atlantic salmon.

SURVIVAL OF JUVENILE ATLANTICS

Once a pair of escaped Atlantic salmon have successfully spawned and their eggs have hatched, the resulting fry begin life as wild fish. Although they are not as genetically adapted as wild salmon to their home streams, they probably respond instinctively to their surroundings. Studies on fry produced by hatchery-raised parents show that they have poorer survival rates than wild populations in the same river.

Juvenile salmon of all species are known to be territorial, and fish that have established their territory first are usually more successful in securing food and cover within that territory. If escaped Atlantics were to spawn later than most Pacific salmon, then the Pacific fry would establish their territory before the Atlantics emerge from the gravel. Atlantic salmon fry are also smaller than Pacific fry, and Pacific salmon grow much faster than Atlantic salmon, so Atlantics are less likely to compete successfully for food, and are more vulnerable to predators. That was the pattern in the Lake Ontario studies. Biologists who have observed Atlantic fry in B.C. streams say that unlike Pacific salmon, which tend to swim up in the water column, Atlantic fry tend to remain on the bottom, lying very still, which makes them easy prey for aggressive predators such as sculpin (also called bullheads).

The survival rates of juvenile Atlantic salmon found in B.C. waters are not known, but by mid-2005, there was no documented case of a juvenile salmon maturing in the wild and returning to spawn.

MATING CONSEQUENCES

It is very unlikely that Atlantic and Pacific salmon will ever successfully interbreed, because they are genetically different. Hybrids between the two have been produced under controlled conditions in the laboratory, but the survival rate was very low. Interbreeding has never been observed in the wild.

Any potential effects of farmed salmon mating with wild salmon are restricted to escaped farmed Pacific salmon mating with wild Pacific salmon. Because farmed salmon have been bred specifically to perform well in a farm environment, mating between farmed and the better-adapted wild fish could compromise the genetic characteristics of wild stocks.

Some 9,600 genetically distinct wild Pacific salmon stocks live in B.C. waters. All have evolved over thousands of years, and each species and each stock is genetically adapted to the environmental conditions of its birth stream. This has given Pacific salmon a great biodiversity. Nature's way of preventing excessive inbreeding within individual year classes is to ensure that a small percentage of every salmon population "wanders" to streams other than their birth streams. This continual introduction of new genetic material is necessary to enhance productivity and adaptability as the salmon stocks evolve, as long as the number of strays between populations is not too great.

B.C. Freshwater Juvenile Atlantic Salmon Sightings and Captures

RIVER	AREA	1996	1997	1998	1999	2000	2001	2002	2003	2004	2005
Adam	12				3						
Amor de Cosmos	12				113	8					
Cameleon Harbour Creek*	13							1			
Carnation*	23		1	3			1	2			
Georgie Lake*	12	41	21	86	30						
Keogh*	12			1	2						
Lake of the Mts. Ck.*	12			3				4			
Lois Lake*	16	13									
Pye*	13		1								
Ritterdon*	23							1			
Stamp*	23						3				
Tsitika	13				24	2	3		1		
Total		54	26	114	150	12	3	8	1	0	0

* Freshwater lake and/or stream in which escapes are believed to be from aquaculture facilities
SOURCE: ATLANTIC SALMON WATCH PROGRAM

In a perfect world, we would allow wild Pacific salmon to evolve naturally. However, since the 1890s, fisheries managers have tried to increase salmon stocks by transplanting salmon eggs and juvenile salmon throughout the Pacific basin.

In the north Pacific ocean, approximately 5 billion fish per year are released into the wild from Canada, Russia, Japan and the U.S.

Invasion and Colonization

The introduction of exotic species, whether intentional or not, can have a significant impact on native organisms and ecosystems. Rabbits in Australia, Nile perch in Africa, and Eurasian water milfoil and purple loosestrife in B.C. are just a few examples. According to the Nature Conservancy (1998), introduced species are responsible for 68 percent of all recent freshwater fish extinctions that have taken place in North America.

Atlantic salmon, an introduced species, have successfully reached fresh water, but they have not established a self-sustaining, or feral, population. To do this, they would have to spawn successfully, which they have been shown to do. Their offspring would have to rear in the fresh water, which they have been shown to do. The juvenile salmon would then have to migrate to salt water, survive for three years, then return and spawn successfully. If the cycle were completed over and over and in sufficient numbers to perpetuate the stock, Atlantic salmon would be considered to have colonized B.C. waters.

Several factors work in favour of colonization. Atlantic salmon can produce more than twice as many eggs as Pacific salmon. Survival rates of those offspring are lower than in wild salmon, and Atlantic salmon are not as genetically adapted to conditions in the wild, but any Atlantic salmon that did hatch would begin life as "wild" fish and respond instinctively to their surroundings. As in native species, the fittest of these would likely survive, and natural selection could eventually produce fish that are better adapted to survival in B.C. waters.

So far there is no evidence of colonization having occurred, either among the 8.6 million Atlantics that were intentionally released for enhancement over the years, or among the approximately one million Atlantic salmon that have escaped from salmon farms during the past 20 years. But none of this means that Atlantic salmon cannot or will not colonize.

In B.C., some 600 million juvenile salmon and cutthroat trout are released into the wild each year from government and community enhancement facilities. According to a 2004 Pacific Fisheries Resource Conservation Council (PFRCC) study, there has not been a consistent overall increase in salmon production or catch in B.C. as a result of these efforts. Some populations of wild salmon have actually declined as enhancement activity has grown.

Because hatchery-raised fish are not exposed to the same challenges as wild fish, they do not have to be as fit to survive. In government enhancement hatcheries, the average survival rate of eggs to the fry stage is between 80 and 95 percent, whereas the survival rate in the wild is less than 15 percent. In other words, only the strongest eggs survive, so when hatchery-produced fish are released into the ocean and breed with wild fish, they can water down the genetic pool of the offspring. In the Strait of Georgia, for example, the PFRCC estimated that up to 70 percent of the fish that spawn are descendants of hatchery-enhanced stock. The genetic uniqueness of the remaining wild stocks is at risk, and so is their very survival.

To complicate matters, many of the stocks used for enhancement come from a few select rivers and a limited number of parents, which further reduces genetic diversity. As well, stocks from those select sources have been transplanted to a number of different watersheds and rivers to which they are not genetically adapted. For example, stocks from Qualicum River salmon have been transplanted to most of the streams on the east coast of Vancouver Island.

Through hatchery enhancement, genetic mixing has been taking place in B.C. for more than 100 years. We do not know how many of the estimated 9,600 wild stocks have maintained their genetic uniqueness because of this practice. The 2004 PFRCC report stated: "Although evidence of actual impacts is scarce, current theory indicates that enhancement could significantly reduce the genetic diversity and fitness of wild salmon." And: "Major hatcheries and spawning channels pose the highest risks to [the continued survival of] wild salmon." The David Suzuki Foundation sustainable fishing project says: "All along the coast, hatchery fish are being added to wild populations. These hatchery fish are less diverse genetically than their wild populations, and once released into nature create the illusion of large, wild stocks. When these stocks are fished, the small group of fish that is truly wild becomes highly vulnerable to extinction. Hatchery fish also compete with wild fish for limited resources. Although meant to enhance our fishery, in the end, large-scale hatcheries could help to destroy it."

In most ways, farmed fish are the same as those used for wild-stock enhancement. They are raised in the same type of hatcheries under the same conditions for some or all of the freshwater stages of their lives. In enhancement hatcheries where fry are fed before release, they are given the same feed as farmed fish. The primary difference is that farmed salmon are held in captivity all their lives, whereas fish raised in enhancement hatcheries are released into the wild. Farmed salmon are also different in that they have been bred selectively for different traits such as genetic uniformity, low aggressiveness, disease resistance, fast growth and general suitability to the netpen environment. These traits make them somewhat less genetically adapted for survival in the wild.

The genetic effects of cross-breeding between wild salmon and enhancement salmon or farmed salmon depends largely on the number of fish that are released into the wild. Since 1987, almost a million chinook and just over 13,000 coho have escaped from B.C. salmon farms. This compares with more than 884 million chinook and over 340 million coho salmon raised and released by B.C. enhancement hatcheries over the same period. By any measure, enhancement-produced salmon have a much greater impact on wild salmon than escapees from salmon farms.

Regardless of the impact of enhancement-produced stocks, the offspring of any farmed salmon that finds a wild mate and spawns successfully will share some new genetic traits. Those changes depend on the genetic differences between the two and, on a larger scale, how much interbreeding goes on between wild and farmed stocks and whether the two are on the spawning beds at the same time. Because it is hard to tell the difference between wild Pacific salmon and farmed Pacifics, we do not know how the two intermingle on the spawning ground or how successful they are at spawning.

Much more information is needed on the impacts of cross-breeding, but some generalizations can be made. A small amount of gene flow from farmed salmon to wild salmon could, like natural wandering in wild populations, have a positive effect on wild stocks. A larger gene flow over an extended period is likely to reduce wild salmon's genetic fitness for survival, and the offspring of wild–farmed crosses would not survive as well as wild salmon. Those "inferior" fish would be less likely to survive to spawn; therefore fewer offspring would be born, fewer would return and so on, and these fish would soon be selected out of the population. Or those offspring could breed with true wild fish and acquire some of the genetic traits that improve their chances of survival.

Between 2000 and 2005, the average number of chinook that escaped from salmon farms each year was just under 7,000, whereas the average number of coho was 26. We do not know how many of those fish have spawned successfully with their wild counterparts. If we consider the number of escaped Atlantics (148,573) and the number of adult Atlantics found in fresh water over those same years (291), and apply that ratio (.002 percent) to the number of escaped chinook, about 80 would return to the spawning beds. If we apply the ratio to coho, less than one fish would make it. Government and industry must continue to prevent escapes as far as possible, but even if the number of reported escapes is significantly underestimated, the 52 million enhancement-produced chinook and 20 million coho released into the wild each year are a much greater threat to the genetic integrity of wild salmon.

SPREAD OF PATHOGENS

When diseased fish escape from a salmon farm, they can spread pathogens to other organisms—if they can survive both the disease and predators (diseased fish are much more vulnerable to predation) long enough to pass on the pathogens. The common predators of salmon—seals, gulls and otters—are not known to be susceptible to salmon diseases, so they are unlikely to carry diseases and pass them on.

Such a pathogen would not likely be very effective. Farmed salmon catch diseases from outside sources—pathogens that are carried by wild salmon or other fish. A new host would have to have contact with the pathogen from the escaped fish in a high enough concentration for a long enough period to become infected. That host would probably have some immunity, as Pacific salmon do, or be healthy enough to fight off the disease. If the fish did become sick, it could only pass the pathogen on if the same conditions were in place.

There is also a chance that a diseased escapee could survive symptoms and predators long enough to find a mate and spawn, and it could then transfer the disease to its offspring.

WE KNOW VERY LITTLE ABOUT THE INTERACTIONS BETWEEN FARMED and wild salmon. Either way, the fewer fish that escape from salmon farms, the smaller the chance of harm to wild stocks. If the industry's reported escape numbers are accurate, they show that salmon farmers have reduced the number of escapes in recent years. This reduction is mirrored by the decreasing number of both adult and juvenile Atlantic salmon found in fresh water.

Few studies have been done and the analysis of the results is mixed. The Salmon Aquaculture Review, completed by the provincial Environmental Assessment Office in 1997, concluded: "The risk of escaped Atlantic salmon causing lasting harm appears to be so low that there is no demonstrable basis at this time for discontinuing their culture in B.C."

But the PFRCC's 2003 report *Making Sense of the Salmon Aquaculture Debate* said that Atlantic salmon can colonize in B.C. rivers: "the extent of these phenomena and their potential to expand in the future is highly uncertain due to data limitations. One would hope that should a population become established, it would likely be quickly targeted and eliminated."

10

DONE LIKE DINNER

Farmed Salmon on the Menu

Fresh, whole farmed salmon, ready for market

PHOTO courtesy B.C. Salmon Farmers Association

FISH HAS LONG BEEN ONE OF THE FIRST CHOICES OF PROTEIN AMONG health-conscious people, and medical studies continue to show that salmon is one of the healthiest fish we can eat. It is an excellent source of high-quality protein and an important source of essential omega-3 fatty acids, and it is low in cholesterol.

However, consumers are understandably unsure whether farmed salmon has all of the health benefits of wild salmon.

CHEFS' CHOICE

Taste is a matter of personal preference. Some chefs prefer wild salmon, some prefer farmed, just as some people prefer cheddar over blue cheese or brie. Five species of Pacific salmon and farmed Atlantic salmon are available to consumers, each with distinct taste, fat and texture characteristics.

The great majority of restaurants around the world that serve salmon choose farmed salmon, which appears on the menu at many fine restaurants as fresh Atlantic salmon. Fresh Pacific salmon simply isn't available in many parts of the world, or it can only be had for a few months of the year, during the salmon harvest. Farmed Atlantic and Pacific salmon are available fresh all year round. Thanks to the constant supply and the abundance of farmed salmon, people who market it have been able to develop a superior distribution system for their products. Throughout the world, it is simply far easier to buy farmed salmon than to buy wild salmon. As well, farmed salmon are much more uniform in size and texture than wild salmon, which makes it easier for restaurant chefs to produce a consistent menu item.

On the west coast, fresh wild salmon is readily available during the summer and fall months when the commercial fleets are harvesting the fish. Chefs have five species to choose from. Sometimes supply is sporadic because of harvesting schedules, and fresh wild Pacific salmon is not readily available in the winter and spring.

Many high-end Vancouver-area restaurants and their chefs serve only wild Pacific salmon and other "organic" menu items. Some chefs are outspoken opponents of salmon farming. Their reasons are the same as those of many opponents. In contrast, few if any restaurants boast about serving fresh farmed salmon. Those that do serve it are more likely simply to advertise fresh coho, chinook or Atlantic salmon without using the word "wild."

In 2004, a blind taste test was conducted by the pro-industry group Salmon of the Americas (SOTA) at the annual meeting of the American Culinary Federation, the largest and most prestigious organization of professional chefs in the U.S.A. In the test, 89 chefs and others associated with the restaurant industry ate samples of fresh wild sockeye and farmed Atlantic salmon, which had been steamed without seasonings. Sixty-six said they preferred the taste of farmed fish. SOTA executive director Alex Trent said that these results are usual for blind taste tests—a majority of consumers prefer the taste of farmed salmon.

In another blind taste test, conducted by a panel of five well-known chefs and food experts for the San Francisco *Chronicle* in February 2005, tasters sampled canned salmon. Their favourite was Kirkland's canned Atlantic salmon from Costco, the only farmed fish among the 17 samples tested.

COMPARATIVE NUTRITIONAL VALUE

Nutritionists, Health Canada, the Canadian Heart and Stroke Foundation and other health professionals recommend that every person consume fish regularly. According to the experts, wild and farmed salmon have comparable nutritional and other health benefits. Health Canada, for example, does not differentiate between them when recommending salmon as a healthy food source. That is because salmon contains a variety of fats, including omega-3 fatty acids. These are polyunsaturated fats—known as essential fatty

How Farmed Salmon Outmarketed Wild Salmon

In 1980, commercial fisheries produced 99 percent of the salmon consumed worldwide, and farmed salmon accounted for only 1 percent. In 2005, 60 percent of the 2 million tonnes (1.8 million tons) of wild and farmed salmon produced annually came from salmon farms.

For B.C., the turning point came in 1998, when the farmed-salmon harvest exceeded the wild catch for the first time. Since then, farmed salmon have made up about 60 percent of the total production of salmon in B.C.

As food markets have become more globalized, it has become more difficult for wild salmon to compete against farmed salmon in the marketplace. Large food retailers and warehouse clubs such as Costco are dominating more of the seafood market and, as Gunner Knapp, a professor of economics at the University of Anchorage discussed at an aquaculture conference in 2003, large-scale retailers require a large, consistent, reliable supply of fish, as well as low, competitive, stable prices, consistent quality and traceability.

Knapp also pointed out that:

+ Wild salmon runs are subject to the vagaries of nature and therefore the catch is inconsistent from year to year and very hard to forecast.
+ In contrast, farmed-salmon production is very predictable. With computer technology, salmon farmers can track the weight and growth rates of the fish daily, in each netpen, and they can plan production for a controlled harvest throughout the year.
+ Large numbers of wild salmon are usually harvested over a very short period, when the fish return to spawn; therefore, much of the catch must be canned and frozen.
+ In contrast, salmon-farming companies can usually wait until they have buyers before harvesting and processing their fish for maximum value.

Many consumers still prefer the taste and colour of wild salmon, and farmed salmon has a certain stigma—people think it is inferior to wild salmon, perhaps because wild fish grow in a freer, more natural state. But, Knapp noted, thanks to aquaculture, customers have grown used to fish that is not only custom-processed but fresher than the wild catch, consistent in quality and always available—conditions that the wild fishery can seldom meet. More and more people are finding salmon at the grocery store at a reasonable price and making it a part of their diet. In the U.S., consumption of salmon has almost doubled, from 1.2 pounds (544 g) per person per year in 1995 to 2 pounds (916 g) in 2002.

But none of the above improves the taste or texture of farmed salmon

Farmed Salmon Production vs. Commercial Salmon Catch

(Landed/Farmgate value $000)

YEAR	FARMED SALMON*	WILD SALMON**
1982	1,136	164,102
1983	708	111,085
1984	702	144,798
1985	820	246,670
1986	2,728	265,774
1987	12,872	212,060
1988	39,084	312,065
1989	59,739	256,081
1990	78,646	263,400
1991	110,913	172,440
1992	115,517	191,799
1993	138,150	201,027
1994	153,815	256,309
1995	170,371	85,698
1996	155,934	99,205
1997	176,228	109,902
1998	228,961	54,007
1999	290,610	26,302
2000	281,696	50,403
2001	270,893	33,300
2002	288,939	55,900
2003	255,800	48,665
2004	202,200	52,459

* Atlantic and chinook salmon
** Chinook, sockeye, coho, pink, chum
SOURCES: B.C. MINISTRY OF AGRICULTURE AND LANDS, AND FISHERIES AND OCEANS CANADA

acids because they are vital to human health. Omega-3 fatty acids are synthesized by marine algae and passed on to fish through the food chain. Humans need to consume omega-3 fatty acids because we do not have the enzymes required to produce sufficient amounts on our own. Omega-3 are found primarily in oily coldwater fish such as salmon, tuna, herring, sardines and mackerel, and in wild game and some plant oils such as flaxseed oil.

Omega-3 fatty acids are proven to help prevent coronary heart disease, the leading cause of death in North America. Health professionals estimate that if everyone ate just two 115-gram (4-oz) servings per week of fatty fish such as salmon, many fewer people would die of sudden cardiac arrest. Omega-3 fatty acids are also known to have beneficial effects on diabetes, arthritis, depression and premature birth. They have been shown to help keep cholesterol and blood triglycerides levels low, reduce blood pressure, slow the rate of blood clotting and reduce the risk of Alzheimer's disease.

Although the omega-3 content in salmon varies by species, food source and the time of year, farmed Atlantic salmon and wild chinook salmon provide higher levels of omega-3 fatty acids than most other fish sources. U.S. Department of Agriculture figures show that farmed Atlantic salmon and wild chinook salmon contain 1.9–2 grams (0.07 oz) each of omega-3 fatty acids per 100 grams (0.02 oz per 1 oz)—the highest of any salmon (see sidebar "Fat Content of Fish and Other Common Foods"). Wild sockeye and farmed coho are next, with 1.3 grams (0.04 oz) each. The figures show that farmed and wild salmon have comparable amounts of omega-3 fatty acids.

Salmon also contain omega-6 fatty acids, which, like omega-3, are considered essential. They are polyunsaturated fats that the body cannot produce on its own. Unlike omega-3, though, omega-6 is found not only in fish but also in grains, plant-based oils, poultry, eggs and processed foods such as cereals, whole-grain bread, baked goods, fried foods and margarine. Omega-6 fatty acids are said to help regulate inflammation and blood pressure as well as heart, gastrointestinal and kidney functions. They are also shown to reduce rheumatoid arthritis, uncomfortable menstrual symptoms, acne and the symptoms of eczema and psoriasis.

Nutritionists have found that a balance between the consumption of omega-3 and omega-6 fatty acids is required for good health. The optimal omega-6 to omega-3 dietary ratio is considered to be about 4:1. The average North American diet has a ratio in excess of 20:1. Dietary sources of omega-3 are critically important, and nutritionists recommend that people lower the amount of surplus omega-6 they are eating. In both farmed and wild salmon, the content of omega-6 fatty acids tends to rise in parallel with omega-3 content, though farmed salmon can contain higher proportions of omega-6 fatty acids.

CHEMICALS IN FARMED SALMON

Like virtually all foods consumed today, wild and farmed salmon both contain trace amounts of persistent organic pollutants. PCBs and other chemicals are a legacy of mankind's industrial activity and unfortunately are present in the aquatic environment throughout the world. They are not "added" to salmon, but sometimes they are found in farmed salmon at levels higher than in wild salmon.

Fat Content of Fish and Other Common Foods
(Grams per 100-gram/3.5-oz serving, raw)

SPECIES	SATURATED FAT	MONO-UNSATURATED FAT	POLY-UNSATURATED FAT	CHOLESTEROL
Farmed Atlantic	2.2	3.8	3.9	.06
Wild Atlantic	1.0	2.1	2.5	.06
Wild Chinook	2.5	4.5	2.1	.05
Farmed Coho	1.8	3.3	1.9	.05
Wild Coho	1.3	2.1	2.0	.05
Wild Chum	0.8	1.5	0.9	.07
Wild Pink	0.6	0.9	1.4	.05
Wild Sockeye	1.5	4.1	1.9	.06
Chicken Breast (meat)	0.3	0.3	0.3	.06

SPECIES	SATURATED FAT	MONO- UNSATURATED FAT	POLY- UNSATURATED FAT	CHOLESTEROL
Chicken Breast (meat/skin)	2.7	3.8	2.0	.06
Chicken Thigh (meat)	1.0	1.2	1.0	.08
Chicken Thigh (meat/skin)	4.4	6.5	3.4	.08
Gr Beef (95% lean)	2.2	2.1	0.2	.06
Gr Beef (75% lean)	9.5	11.	0.6	.07
Pork Loin, Separable (lean & fat)	4.4	5.6	1.3	.06

Note: The fat content of wild salmon can vary from 5 to 15 percent depending on age and season.
SOURCE: UNITED STATES DEPARTMENT OF AGRICULTURE NUTRIENT DATABASE FOR STANDARD REFERENCE, RELEASE 16-1 (2004).

Omega-3 Content of Common Foods

(Grams per 100-gram/3.5-oz serving, raw)

SPECIES	OMEGA-3 (GRAMS)
Mackerel (Jack/Pacific)	1.5
Farmed Atlantic	2.0
Wild Atlantic	1.7
Wild Chinook	2.0
Farmed Coho	1.3
Wild Coho	1.2
Wild Chum	0.6
Wild Pink	1.0
Wild Sockeye	1.3
Fresh Yellowfin Tuna	0.5
Flounder	0.2
Chicken (breast, meat only)	<0.1
Ground Beef	<0.1

Note: The fat content of wild salmon can vary from 5 to 15 percent, depending on age and season.
SOURCE: UNITED STATES DEPARTMENT OF AGRICULTURE NUTRIENT DATABASE FOR STANDARD REFERENCE, RELEASE 16-1 (2004).

As with most other farmed animals (and humans), farm-raised salmon are sometimes treated with drugs when they get sick. They are also fed natural pigments or synthetic versions of natural pigments to provide essential nutrients and to colour their flesh to enhance market appeal.

PERSISTENT ORGANIC POLLUTANTS

Persistent organic pollutants (POPs) are chemicals that share certain characteristics. They are typically manufactured compounds, and many are highly toxic. They persist in the environment and accumulate in living organisms, typically in the fatty tissues. Because they degrade slowly and can evaporate and condense repeatedly, they have found their way to the far corners of the earth, including the most remote polar regions. They are present in the air we breathe, our rivers and oceans, sediments and soil. They are in nearly all the foods we eat—milk, beef, chicken, pork, fish, vegetables and fruit.

As it becomes possible to detect smaller and smaller amounts of chemicals in the environment, traces of POPs are found in more and more food products. Scientists can now measure residues as small as parts per billion and even parts per trillion. One ppb is equivalent to a single drop of a chemical in a 500,000-litre (110,000-gallon) Olympic-size swimming pool, or one pinch of salt in 10 tons (9 tonnes) of potato chips.

Most POPs are industrial chemicals or pesticides. They include dieldrin, DDT, toxaphene, polychlorinated biphenyls (PCBs), polybrominated diphenyl ethers (PBDEs), polychlorinated dibenzodioxins (dioxin) and polychlorinated furans (furans). Most of them were invented for specific uses in farming or manufacturing, but some, including dioxins and furans, are by-products of combustion and industrial processes, or natural phenomena such as forest fires and volcanic eruptions.

Other chemicals and toxic metals that occur naturally in the environment are also found in the blood and fat of fish and other animals, including humans. These include mercury, arsenic, cadmium, selenium (an essential nutrient at low concentrations, but toxic at high concentrations) and tributyltin (TBT)—a tin-based anti-fouling treatment used in marine waters.

Oceans play an integral role in the circulation and deposit of POPs, by functioning as giant sinks for the deposit of contaminants. From the smallest bacteria to the largest whale, each organism in the sea accumulates all the contaminants that their prey has consumed. The higher the animal is on the food chain, the more toxins it accumulates. The same goes for fat content. Carnivorous predators, which are at the top of the food chain, usually contain more PCBs than those lower on the food chain. A year 2000 study on contaminants in the flesh of wide-roaming transient as well as resident killer whales in the Puget Sound and the southern Strait of Georgia found them to have such high levels of PCBs that whale researchers dubbed them "the most contaminated marine mammals in the world."

Although marine organisms also pick up minor accumulations from contaminants suspended in the water column, both wild and farmed salmon absorb most PCBs from their feed—wild salmon from plankton, shrimp, small fish and other prey, and farmed salmon from the fish that were processed to manufacture their feed. Because Atlantic and some Pacific salmon species are relatively fatty, they usually accumulate more contaminants than less fatty fish.

Whether or not we eat salmon, we cannot avoid ingesting POPs. For example, salmon contains PCBs but so does virtually everything else we eat, and salted butter, canned tuna in oil, roasted chicken and homemade brown gravy contain more PCBs than salmon.

All humans have POPs in their bodies. Yet we know almost nothing about how these chemicals affect our health, except that it is safe to assume POPs are not beneficial.

PCBs

Polychlorinated biphenyls (PCBs) are a family of oily chemical substances that were manufactured beginning in the 1930s. They were developed for the electricity supply industry. PCBs were stable and not very volatile, therefore well suited to their use as lubricants and coolants in electrical transformers and capacitors. They were also used to make plastics, paints, inks, carbon-free copy paper and other products. PCBs were banned from use in the manufacture of equipment in the U.S. in 1976 after research showed that they could cause cancer and numerous other health problems in laboratory animals.

Scientists estimate that as many as two-thirds of all PCBs ever produced are still present in the environment. They are still being used in electrical equipment, and they are buried in landfills. They are found in all foods that come from animals. It is likely that the body of every person in North America and the rest of the world has accumulated PCBs and other persistent organic pollutants.

No one has ever proven a link between PCBs and cancer in humans, but many government agencies such as the U.S. Environmental Protection Agency, the International Agency for Research on Cancer and the National Toxicology Program consider PCBs "probable," or "likely" to cause cancer in people.

The report *Global Assessment of Organic Contaminants in Farmed Salmon*, authored by Ronald Hites et al. and published in the January 2004 issue of the journal *Science*, received a great deal of worldwide attention. The authors had tested farmed salmon and had found higher levels of contaminants, most notably PCBs, than in the wild salmon they tested.

Numerous other studies have compared the level of contaminants in wild and farmed salmon. The studies show slightly different levels of contaminants, but all of the results are similar to Hites' findings: average PCB levels of 32 parts per billion (ppb) in British Columbia farm-raised Atlantic salmon, and an average of 4.8 ppb in wild Pacific salmon. (Farmed Pacific salmon were not analyzed.)

However, the levels of contaminants found in the farmed salmon were significantly less than 2 percent of the maximum allowed in food products by the Canadian Food Inspection Agency (CFIA), the U.S. Food and Drug Administration (FDA) and the World Health Organization. Those agencies have set the maximum allowable content at 2,000 ppb—a significant difference from either 4.8 or 32 ppb.

Published studies of PCB levels in wild fish in Alaska and Washington State found very different numbers than Hites et al. In the year 2000, the Circumpolar Conservation Union found sockeye in Alaska's Copper River to have PCB levels of 670 ppb and higher. A 1998 study for the Washington State Department of Fish and Wildlife showed that chinook salmon in Puget Sound, Washington, had PCB levels of 74 ppb and coho had levels of 35 ppb. A study on PCB levels in wild and farmed salmon, commissioned in October 2004 by Salmon

The European Food Safety Authority has concluded that with regard to the health and safety of the consumer, there is no difference between wild and farmed salmon.

PHOTO courtesy B.C. Salmon Farmers Association

of the Americas, showed PCB levels in farmed and wild salmon to be much closer to each other than the Hites report. Farmed salmon from Canada (and Chile), wild Alaska chinook and sockeye salmon all had similar levels. That study found farmed salmon to have concentrations of 11.5 ppb, and a study undertaken by the Alaska Department of Environmental Conservation in 2005 found PCB levels of 10 ppb in wild sockeye and 8.2 ppb in wild chinook.

No salmon—wild or farmed—tested anywhere near the maximum levels of 2,000 ppb set by the major international regulatory agencies.

The presence of PCBs in wild salmon has not raised any warnings about the consumption of wild fish, yet the PCB levels in farmed salmon made headlines around the world. That is because the authors compared their results with the much lower risk-based "consumption advice" level of 6 ppb for PCBs established by the U.S. Environmental Protection Agency. When that level is exceeded, the EPA advises sport and sustenance fishermen to eat no more than one meal of farmed salmon per month. Levels of PCBs that were well within international standards set by the CFIA, FDA, American National Cancer Institute and a host of other scientists, were reported as being 500 percent higher than the EPA benchmark. The authors felt the EPA numbers more accurately reflected the point at which contaminants become hazardous to health, because the EPA addressed the combined effects of a number of contaminants, whereas the other international agencies did not.

The salmon-farming industry pointed out that the EPA weighs only the risks in setting its limits; the FDA weighs both the risks and the health benefits. They argued that the lower EPA levels were designed for sport and subsistence fishermen such as First Nations people who regularly consume large numbers of fish taken from freshwater lakes and streams that are often heavily contaminated. Were the EPA's 6 ppb benchmark accepted by the CFIA, FDA, U.S. National Academy of Science and other institutions, a great deal of the world's harvest of wild salmon (and many other foods) would also be considered unsafe.

The authors of the Hite report concluded that people are more likely to get sick from a fish with PCB levels of 5 ppb than from a fish with 32 ppb. Other agencies, including Health Canada, the FDA and the World Health Organization, recommend both farmed and wild salmon in their literature on the benefits of eating fish. Therefore, it is difficult to say that farmed salmon is any more or less healthy to eat than wild salmon.

Meanwhile, if we are concerned about PCBs in food, we would do well to stop eating a number of other foods before eliminating farmed salmon from our diet. North Americans consume many more PCBs per capita by eating beef, poultry and milk than by eating farmed or wild salmon (see sidebar "PCBs in Our Food").

PBDEs

PBDEs (polybrominated diphenyl ethers) are toxic, man-made, flame-retardant chemicals used in the manufacture of everything from car parts to electronics to upholstery, including furniture cushions, synthetic fabrics, textiles, plastics, carpet backing, electrical insulation, computer and television casings and other items. PBDEs find their way into the environment during manufacturing

PCBs in Our Food

Persistent organic pollutants are everywhere in our food—in beef, poultry, milk and other dairy products as well as fruit and vegetables.

The first table below shows levels of PCBs in farmed salmon and in other common foods, based on average per capita consumption in the U.S. As shown, salmon accounts for about 6 percent of the PCBs consumed by the average person. The PCBs ingested by eating beef in the average diet account for more than 7 times that found in salmon, milk gives us almost 3 times more PCBs and poultry 50 percent more PCBs.

Annual Per Capita Load of PCBs by Food*

FOOD ITEM	PICTOGRAMS TEQ [toxic equivalents]
beef	2016
milk	756
poultry	386
farmed salmon	275
pork	207

PCBs in Other Foods**

FOOD ITEM	PARTS PER BILLION
butter, salted	70
tuna, canned in oil	45
chicken breast, roasted	32
brown gravy, homemade	30
salmon steak, baked	26
pancakes, from mix	24
meatloaf	23
beef steak, pan cooked	22
pork chop, pan cooked	21
egg, fried	19

FOOD ITEM	PARTS PER BILLION
pork roast, baked	18
popcorn, popped in oil	17
biscuit, refrigerated dough, baked	16
veal cutlet, pan cooked	13
cornbread	11
English muffin, plain, toasted	10
raisin	10
chicken, fried	9
caramel candy	6

* Based on Environmental Working Group report, July 2003
** UNITED STATES DEPARTMENT OF AGRICULTURE NUTRIENT DATABASE FOR STANDARD REFERENCE, RELEASE 16 (2003)

and processing, and through "off-gassing." They have been in use since the 1980s and, like many other artificial compounds, are found in the air, water and land. Human breast milk, human blood and all foods of animal origin contain PBDEs.

No human studies on the effects of PBDEs have been carried out, and no tolerances for them have been established by regulation in North America or Europe. However, studies show that levels of PBDEs in humans are rising dramatically, and health experts are concerned about potential impacts.

Fish are also shown to contain PBDEs. As with other persistent organic pollutants, they ingest PBDEs with feed and accumulate them in their fatty tissue. A 2004 Health Canada study found farmed salmon to contain 1.6 ppb and wild salmon 0.7 ppb. In a follow-up to their 2004 *Science* study, Hites et al. measured levels of PBDEs in wild and farmed salmon. The results were published in the journal *Environmental Science and Technology*. The Hites group found similar results to the Health Canada and other studies, but surprisingly they also found that wild B.C. chinook salmon contained twice the PBDEs (4 ppb) of farmed B.C. Atlantics (2 ppb). Other wild B.C. salmon examined contained less than 1 ppb. Salmon of the Americas also studied PBDEs. They found levels of 0.4–5.5 ppb in farmed salmon, and 0.2–2.8 ppb in wild salmon. Another study found wild halibut to contain 2–28 ppb. By comparison, household dust contains 1,000–5,000 ppb. *(but we don't eat dust)*

Health Canada, one of the first agencies in the world to monitor for PBDEs in various foods, found "no evidence that current levels of PBDEs in the environment are harming human health at the moment." They concluded: "Health Canada's opinion is that the current levels found in any retail food are not considered to be a health concern." With no data on the impact of PBDEs, and no limits on the production or use of PBDEs, we can expect levels to continue to rise in all of the organisms around us, including the foods we eat.

DRUGS AND FARMED SALMON

Most farmed salmon are vaccinated as smolts against the common bacterial pathogens they will be exposed to in the wild. However, when they become sick or require treatment for sea lice, a veterinarian prescribes the appropriate drug to be mixed into the feed by the feed manufacturer. Once treated, the fish cannot be harvested for a specified period of time, to ensure that any trace of the drug remaining in the flesh of the fish is within standards established by Health Canada.

Antibiotics

To protect consumers who are allergic to antibiotics, regulations require that when farmed salmon are treated with antibiotics, they must not be harvested until the drug is fully metabolized. This can take up to 180 days. The CFIA, which monitors food safety, conducts spot audits of fish products to test for drug residues. To date, fewer than 1 percent of the fish inspected by CFIA have contained levels of antibiotics above the minimum set by Health Canada. Those levels have ranged from 0.14 to 0.5 ppm; the maximum level is 0.1 ppm.

Anti-Parasite Drugs

Once farmed salmon are treated for sea lice, they must not be harvested for at least 25 days to ensure that they are drug-free. In B.C., the CFIA monitors harvested farmed salmon for residues of emamectin benzoate (SLICE), the anti-sea lice drug of choice. The maximum residue level, set by Health Canada, is 50 ppb—half the maximum allowed in Europe, the U.K. and Chile. CFIA has not reported any case of farmed salmon in B.C. containing levels of SLICE above the Health Canada maximum.

Malachite Green

The copper-based fungicide known as malachite green was used for decades by salmon farmers and Fisheries and Oceans Canada (DFO) enhancement hatcheries to control parasites and fungus on fish eggs, but was identified as a carcinogen by Health Canada in the early 1990s and banned for use on fish for human consumption.

In 2005, traces of malachite green were detected in the flesh of farmed salmon at two B.C. salmon farms. Salmon farmers insisted they had not used malachite green in many years. A few weeks later researchers tested wild salmon and found that they had similar traces of the chemical.

Health Canada has a zero-tolerance policy for malachite green—no detectable amount is allowed in food intended for humans. The contaminated fish contained levels of 0.31 to 1.3 ppb. Other countries are less stringent: Japan allows 5 ppb and the European Union allows 2 ppb. Recent U.S. FDA studies have found that laboratory rats had to have levels of at least 91,000 ppb of malachite green before they showed an increasing tendency to develop tumours.

The source of the contamination has not yet been discovered, but malachite green is persistent in the environment and could potentially have stayed in the land, water and/or structures at salmon farms and fish hatcheries since the years when it was in common use. Over many decades, billions of hatchery fish were treated with malachite green and released into the wild (and consumed by humans). Hatchery fish may even have helped spread the chemical into the environment. As well, malachite green is still used in the manufacture of paper, textiles, mosquito coils and other non-food items, so it is still entering the environment. In 2005, salmon sold at a grocery store chain in Europe was discovered to contain trace levels of malachite green. The culprit turned out to be not the salmon farms, but the green hand towels being used in the seafood department.

In spite of its policy that no trace of malachite green is acceptable, Health Canada did not issue a recall for the farmed salmon found to contain malachite green in 2005. Officials noted that the chances of serious harm to human health were remote. The U.K. Veterinary Residues Committee has also told consumers that they are not at risk from eating farmed salmon that contained 4.9 ppb. The U.K. Department for Environment, Food and Rural Affairs confirmed that these quantities are so minimal that they would have no impact whatsoever on humans.

The presence of malachite green in both wild and farmed salmon could cause a dilemma for Health Canada and the CFIA. If they were to maintain and enforce their zero-tolerance levels, they would have to shut down both the commercial salmon-fishing industry and the salmon-farming industry.

Hormones

Hormones are not used in any form in any salmon destined for human consumption.

Pigments

Astaxanthin and canthaxanthin are carotenoids that occur naturally in marine algae and tiny crustaceans such as krill and shrimp, which feed on algae. Carotenoids are nutrients required by most living organisms for proper growth. When wild salmon eat these crustaceans, they gain their pink or red colouring. Because farmed salmon do not eat wild feed, and because these natural pigments are usually lost during the processing of fish feed, a natural or synthetic version of these chemicals is added to feed to colour their flesh. Feed manufacturers say that the synthetic versions of astaxanthin and canthaxanthin are chemically identical to the natural compounds. They say that in B.C., these pigments are added at levels comparable to those of wild salmon and well below the maximum levels recommended by CFIA and the FDA, which approve and regulate their use. Because astaxanthin and canthaxanthin are also powerful antioxidants, they are nutritional for fish and they help extend the shelf life of feed. Government regulations require they be included in fish feed.

Monitoring Residues

To ensure that there are no harmful residues of drugs and chemicals in products destined for human consumption, numerous regulatory measures have been put in place to monitor all agricultural products, including farmed salmon.

In Canada, Health Canada sets the standards for food health and safety, and the Canadian Food Inspection Agency (CFIA) monitors for compliance. The CFIA, under the federal *Fish Inspection Act*, is responsible for ensuring that all fish and seafood for export meet national quality standards.

The provincial Ministry of Agriculture and Lands (MAL), under the *Fish Inspection Act*, is responsible for the inspection of fish processed and sold in B.C. MAL requires all farmed salmon to be processed in a federally and provincially licensed establishment. When salmon are transported to a processing plant, an affidavit must go with them, documenting detailed tracking information and listing any drugs that may have been used to treat the fish.

All fish for export must be processed at a plant where an approved Quality Monitoring Program (QMP) is in place. A QMP is a plant-based self-monitoring and inspection program based on the requirements of the Hazard Analysis Critical Control Point (HACCP) Plan. HACCP plans consist of measures that food processors take to ensure food safety. One such measure is regular drug testing by the plant to make sure that the mandatory drug withdrawal period has been observed for any fish treated with drugs, and that the fish are drug-free. Allowing any industry to monitor itself may be like asking the fox to guard the chicken house, but CFIA says its inspectors regularly test for drugs, audit the processors' QMPs and verify compliance with regulations and policies.

If fish are found to contain unacceptable drug residues, efforts are made to halt the sale of the product or, in some cases, to recall it. This does not always occur. By the time the samples are analyzed for drugs and the report is made, any fish that are contaminated may already have been processed, distributed and consumed. However, fish inspectors say that when drug residues are found, they have been so minute that even a minor allergic reaction is highly unlikely. The CFIA says that it has never received a report of any person becoming ill from consuming drug residues in farmed salmon.

The CFIA also administers the Food Safety Investigation Program, under which it investigates consumer and industry complaints and takes appropriate enforcement actions to help ensure the safety of foods.

They shouldn't be released for market until tests are complete

FISH DISEASE AND HUMANS

Any food not handled or prepared properly can cause people to get sick. The cautions are the same for all seafood and other food products, wild or farmed.

The viral, bacterial and fungal diseases that affect farmed salmon have never been shown to affect humans, because fish are cold-blooded and humans are more vulnerable to pathogens specific to warm-blooded hosts, such as cows, pigs, sheep and poultry. Fecal coliform bacteria, for example, are only produced by warm-blooded animals.

There are a few exceptions, though they are not specific to farmed salmon. One of them is the *Vibrio vulnificans* bacteria carried by oysters. It can cause illness in humans who eat raw oysters. Wild or farmed fish can carry *Vibrio* in their mouths or skin, but when a fish carrying *Vibrio* is cooked or frozen for sushi, the bacteria is destroyed. *(but sushi is not cooked or frozen)*

Some species of the bacteria *Aeromonas*, such as *Aeromonas hydrophyla*, can also cause disease in humans. This pathogen, which is generally ingested through natural sources of drinking water, may be a pathogen to salmon in fresh water, but it is not found in either wild or farmed salmon in salt water.

When it comes to internal parasites, farmed salmon have the advantage. Parasites such as anisakine worms and tapeworms *Anisakis simplex* are picked up by wild salmon in their prey and can cause sickness in people who eat raw or undercooked salmon that has not been frozen. Because farmed fish are fed pellets manufactured by heat extrusion—a process that kills parasites—they do not normally carry them.

The internal parasite kudoa affects wild and farmed fish and causes softening of the flesh, but it has no known consequences to human health. Sea lice occur on both wild and farmed salmon. They are removed during processing and are harmless to humans. (For more on diseases and parasites, see Chapter 6.)

HEALTH BENEFITS AND RISKS

In 2004, the European Parliament requested that the European Food Safety Authority (EFSA) assess the health risks associated with the human consumption of wild and farmed fish. The EFSA concluded that if there were any differences between farmed and wild fish, they were small, and that with regard to the health and safety of the consumer, there was no difference between wild and farmed fish.

Canadian and American health officials and agencies have also said that there is no reason for people to limit their consumption of salmon—farmed or wild. The Canadian Heart Foundation and the American Heart Association recommend eating two servings of fatty fish such as salmon every week to lower the risk of coronary heart disease. For people who have had a heart attack, these groups recommend 1 gram (0.04 oz) of omega-3 fatty acid per day. The only recognized organization that would have people eat less is the EPA, whose guidelines say that when fish contain more than 6 ppb of PCBs, people should limit their consumption of farm-raised Atlantic salmon to one meal per month. If that standard were applied to wild salmon as well, the same limit would be placed on many of Alaska's wild sockeye (including Copper River sockeye) and chinook salmon, Puget Sound's chinook and coho, and some B.C. sockeye and chinook stocks—all of which have been shown to contain more than 6 ppb.

The optimal level of contaminants in all of our food is zero. Much more research and innovation are needed to clean up the earth's plants and animals and to produce the goods we want without harming the health of all the world's organisms, including ourselves. In the meantime, the science we do have shows that the amount and type of contaminants found in farmed salmon are not very different from those found in wild salmon or many of the other foods we eat much more frequently. That is why the National Academy of Sciences, the American Heart Association and the World Health Organization all encourage us to eat fish regularly, saying that the benefits of eating a variety of fish far outweigh any health risks.

Afterword: Measuring the Impacts

EVER SINCE HUMANS BEGAN TO GROW CROPS AND RAISE LIVESTOCK, we have been changing the environment. As the world's population grew, so did the demand for agricultural products, and more and more land was converted from its natural state to grow single crops. As fertile land became scarce, our efforts became more concentrated: pesticides and fertilizers were used to gain the largest yield from the smallest area, and factory farms replaced the open range to increase efficiency even more. When fishermen caught most of the wild fish in our oceans, we turned to farming seafood. In almost all of these endeavours, we have polluted the land and sea so badly that the flesh of every living creature contains a dangerous cocktail of man-made poisons. By any measure, humankind has not been a good steward of the earth or its resources.

Almost all of the food North Americans eat today is farmed or manufactured, and the farming of crops and livestock takes a serious toll on the environment. Salmon farming, one of British Columbia's newest agriculture industries, is no exception. That is why some salmon-farming opponents argue that we should not allow aquaculture to take place unless it poses no risk to the aquatic environment. If they are right—and who would disagree in principle?—it would make sense to apply the same set of standards to all land-based agriculture and food processing, and we would have to shut down almost all of our food industries.

Salmon farming has the potential to help meet the increasing worldwide demand for seafood, and to do so on a sustainable and environmentally sound basis. And because it is a relatively new food-producing industry and has been monitored closely since it began in B.C., it can be operated and regulated in such a way that it does not add to the damage we've allowed in other industrial activity. All farming affects the ecosystem it touches. Our task is to define "acceptable" impacts.

We know that the pathogens that make farmed salmon sick come from wild fish, and that when farmed salmon become diseased, they shed large numbers of those pathogens back into the water column. We know that where there are salmon farms whose populations have sea lice, more sea lice are shed into the water than in places without salmon farms. We know that salmon held in netpens produce a great deal of feces and that salmon-farm waste can cause significant changes to the biota in bottom sediments. We know that some farmed Atlantic salmon have escaped from their pens and have spawned and could possibly colonize our rivers. We know that antibiotics and other chemicals are sometimes used to treat sick farmed fish or to eliminate sea lice, and we know little about their impact on the aquatic ecosystem.

However, after 25 years of salmon farming in B.C., we also have no clear evidence that any of these circumstances is hurting wild fish or causing permanent harm to the aquatic environment. We know that the netpens in use at any given time in B.C. take up only about 1 square kilometre (0.4 sq mi). We have found no evidence that sea lice cause declines in wild salmon populations. Salmon farms have not been shown to cause disease epidemics in wild fish. We know that feces and salmon-farm waste have only a temporary impact on the biota of the ocean floor and the bottom begins to revert to its natural makeup as soon as the fish are removed. Escaped Atlantic salmon have not colonized our rivers or even survived in significant numbers.

However, there is clearly a gap between the observed impacts to date and the potential impacts, and this has caused vigorous controversy and extreme polarization among British Columbians. Those opposed to salmon farming believe that the impacts are greater than observed, and supporters believe that current research is proof of minimal impacts. No one knows for sure.

[Then I wasted my time reading this book!]

What we do know is that aquaculture now supplies one-third of the world's seafood, that 75 percent of the world's capture fisheries are at or near their maximum exploitation rates, and that demand for seafood is rising every year. After many decades of trying to rebuild wild stocks, it is doubtful that we can ever rebuild them to the point where fish farming is not needed.

British Columbia, because of its cold, clean water and its well-flushed and well-protected waterways, is ideal for farming salmon. Both our provincial and federal governments have the political will to support the industry, which provides jobs and contributes to an economy that has taken some heavy blows over the last three decades. So, unless the industry finds it is no longer economically viable to do business in B.C., salmon farming—or the farming of other cold-water species—is here to stay.

It is likely that salmon farming in B.C. will continue to take place in open netpens. Salmon can be raised on land, in closed containment systems or in closed bags suspended in salt water. In such systems, waste water can be filtered and recycled, and solid waste can be collected and used as fertilizer. Those environmental impacts are then removed from the aquatic ecosystem. Closed systems also minimize escapes, interactions between farmed salmon and predators, and pathogen transfers to wild stocks. But several pilot projects undertaken in B.C. to test this method have shown that it is not feasible—in B.C. or elsewhere in the world—because of the high cost of land (for land-based systems), tanks, pumping equipment, electricity to control temperatures, and oxygen to be added to the recirculated water. As well, several environmental concerns remain with closed containment systems: the same feed is used, the same drugs are given to fish that get sick and the salmon are raised in higher densities than in open netpens.

For all of these reasons, it is important that British Columbians inform ourselves and support continuing research into wild and farmed salmon, and the aquatic environment.

B.C. must rely mostly on its own research to determine environmental impacts of aquaculture. Salmon farming has been taking place in Norway for almost 50 years, but the lessons learned by European researchers cannot necessarily be applied in B.C. For example, Europeans are raising Atlantic salmon in an environment where Atlantics are the native species and are far outnumbered by their farmed counterparts—a situation quite different from that in B.C.

Research is expensive, and a great deal of it is still needed to understand the dynamics of wild salmon—the natural occurrence of disease, interactions with sea lice and so on—to collect baseline data that can be used to determine how salmon farming is affecting them. Almost everything we know about the impacts of salmon farming comes from government and industry research. It would be patently unfair to question the integrity of government scientists—particularly the scientists at the Pacific Biological Station of Fisheries and Oceans Canada (DFO), who are recognized as among the finest in the world—but their political masters have their own pressures. So does the salmon-farming industry and the groups opposed to aquaculture.

Meanwhile, constant public pressure has kept the spotlight on the industry, which can be a positive force. Most land-based agriculture takes place on private property, but most aquaculture—including salmon farming—takes place on public land—our oceans. The public has the right, and indeed the obligation, to scrutinize the industry for its potential impacts on our aquatic environment. Some of the groundbreaking sea-lice research currently underway, for instance, would not likely have been done had it not been for opponents such as Alexandra Morton who sounded alarms. Industry also reacted and is now monitoring for sea lice, which is adding a great deal to our body of knowledge. Most B.C. salmon farmers are also concerned about the environment and have a real desire to cause as little impact as possible. It is also in their best economic interest to operate on a sustainable basis. Both farmed and wild salmon need a healthy environment, and should the salmon farmer degrade that environment, his stock will be the first to die.

Meanwhile, it is important that British Columbians continue to pay attention—to learn as much as we can, to support intensive and ongoing research, and to apply the results in a way that minimizes damage to our waterways. The more we all know, the better decisions we can make.

Acknowledgements

Hundreds of people were interviewed and/or provided information for the book in other ways. Special thanks are due to several key people who were patient with my endless phone calls and questions. Peter Chettleburgh, editor of *Northern Aquaculture*, provided me with initial contacts in government and industry. Betty Keller, friend and co-author with Rosella Leslie of *Sea-Silver: Inside British Columbia's Salmon-Farming Industry*, allowed me to use material from their book to build my chapter on the history of salmon farming. Greg Deacon of Skretting provided much of the background information for the chapter on fish feed. Dr. Simon Jones of the Pacific Biological Station and Alexandra Morton were the primary sources for information on sea lice. Dr. Stephen F. Cross of Aquametrix Research was my primary source for Chapter 8, on salmon waste and pollution. Joanne Constantine and Andrea Osborne, veterinarians with the Ministry of Agriculture and Lands, provided much of the information for the chapter on disease. Andrew J. L. Thomson of the Atlantic Salmon Watch Program (Fisheries and Oceans Canada) was generous with his time while I was compiling Chapter 9 on farmed-salmon escapes. Gavin Last of the Ministry of Agriculture and Lands was my key contact regarding salmon-farm siting regulations. Gary Caine, also of the Ministry of Agriculture and Lands, helped with industry contacts and provided essential information on a range of government-related issues. Nicky Haigh, head of the Harmful Algae Monitoring Program, deserves credit for teaching me about plankton and plankton blooms. Klaus Schallie of the Canadian Food Inspection Agency provided information about food safety and monitoring for drug residues. Doug Louvier of Wavemaster Canada explained salmon-farm construction and taught me all about nets. Special thanks are also due to Dr. David Groves of Sea Spring Salmon Farms, who was one of the pioneers of salmon farming on the B.C. coast and fielded endless questions on a range of topics.

I also thank the people who let me visit working salmon farms and who were extremely patient with my frequent phone calls about how things work. Clare Backman of Stolt Sea Farm (now merged with Marine Harvest Canada), Ted Needham of Heritage Salmon (now Mainstream Canada), Ian Roberts of Marine Harvest, Bernie Bennett and Joyce Francis of Target Marine and Dave Stover of Browns Bay Packing were particularly helpful. Thanks to Cheryl Thompson and the captain and crew of the coastal freighter *Klassen* for allowing me aboard for several days while they delivered feed to salmon farms.

Researchers who helped with some of the legwork included Shane McCune, Rebecca Salton, Quentin Dodd, Karen Schendlinger and Andrea Wilkinson.

Any writer worth his salt knows that a good editor is the one person that can stop him from sounding too much like an idiot and ending up with egg all over his face. I know, because Mary Schendlinger has been the editor for each of my previous books and has made me look like a much better writer than I am each time. She is a delight to work with and I owe her an eternal debt of gratitude.

Last but not least, very special thanks to my lovely wife, Sage, who not only helped compile the book's many statistics, but put up with endless days when I was either locked up in my home office or disappearing upcoast during the three years it took to put this book together. Without her support, this book could not have been written.

Glossary

acoustic deterrent devices: instruments that emit a loud underwater noise designed to scare away predators such as seals and sea lions.

Agriculture and Agri-Food Canada: the federal agency that co-manages the fish and seafood industry with Fisheries and Oceans Canada (DFO), and that regulates the use of vaccines.

alevin: the life stage of a salmon once it hatches and begins feeding on its egg sac. When the egg sac has been consumed, the fish becomes a fry.

algae: *see* plankton.

algae bloom: *see* plankton bloom.

antibiotic resistance: the resistance of bacteria to drugs that have been used specifically to control them.

antioxidants: essential chemicals that remove potentially damaging oxidizing agents in living cells.

aquaculture: the controlled cultivation and harvest of aquatic plants or animals.

Aquaculture Licence: A licence to operate a salmon farm, issued by the provincial government.

Aquaflor (florfenicol): A broad-spectrum antibiotic, one of four antibiotics licensed for use at B.C. salmon farms.

astaxanthin: a carotenoid and essential nutrient, found in fish such as krill and shrimp. Wild salmon get their colour from consuming prey that contain astaxanthin. Natural or synthetic versions are used in fish feed for farmed salmon to make their flesh redder and more appealing.

bacterial kidney disease (BKD): a disease caused by the bacteria *Renibacterium salmoninarum.* BKD occurs naturally and is prevalent in wild Pacific salmon. For farms raising chinook and coho, BKD is probably the most significant cause of mortality.

benthic community: the collective organisms inhabiting the seabed.

biota: the animals, plants and microbes that inhabit a particular location or region.

blood water: the liquid mix of blood and water produced when fish are killed.

breaking the disease cycle: the process of fallowing a salmon farm site (leaving it empty) for a period of time to eliminate any pathogens from the previous generation of fish.

British Columbia Salmon Farmers Association (BCSFA): an industry association mandated to promote salmon farming in B.C.

broodstock: fish that are used (and often raised) to provide eggs and sperm for the next generation of fish.

Bureau of Veterinary Drugs: a federal agency that operates under the Health Protection Branch of Health Canada, responsible for ensuring that drugs registered and regulated in Canada are safe and effective and do not leave potentially harmful residues in food products. The bureau administers the federal *Food and Drug Act*, which authorizes the sale and use of drugs in Canada for particular species and health conditions.

bycatch: fish caught inadvertently during the harvest of other species, usually in commercial fisheries, and often discarded.

Caligus clemensi **(Caligus)**: a species of sea lice that targets a wide variety of aquatic fish and can move to different hosts.

Canadian Environmental Assessment Agency: An independent federal body, accountable to Parliament through the Minister of the Environment. The agency works to "provide Canadians with high-quality environmental assessments that contribute to informed decision making, in support of sustainable development."

Canadian Food Inspection Agency (CFIA): an independent government agency mandated to safeguard Canada's food supply. The CFIA, which operates under the federal *Fish Inspection Act*, is responsible for the inspection of farmed fish for export to ensure that all fish and seafood meet national quality standards. Health Canada sets the standards for food health and safety, and the CFIA monitors for compliance.

canthaxanthin: a carotenoid and essential nutrient found in many fruits, vegetables and flowers. Natural or synthetic versions are used in fish feed for farmed salmon to make their flesh redder and more appealing.

capture fishery: a commercial fishing activity in which wild fish are captured (as opposed to aquaculture).

carotenoids: a class of pigments that are synthesized in leaves, flowers, fruits and vegetables, giving them their colour. Beta-carotene, the pigment that makes carrots orange, is the best-known carotenoid. Carotenoids are essential nutrients for all living organisms. Plants such as phytoplankton are the source of carotenoids for fish.

combi-tank: a circular tank for incubating fish. The tank contains an artificial substrate that mimics natural spawning gravel.

enhancement hatchery: a facility raised to enhance wild stocks.

enteric redmouth disease: a disease caused by the bacterial pathogen *Yersinia ruckeri*, which affects both wild and farmed Pacific salmon as well as farmed Atlantic salmon, primarily in fresh water.

environmental disease: a disease caused by a pathogen that occurs naturally in the environment.

exotic disease: a disease that does not occur naturally in the environment in which it is found.

eyed stage: the developmental stage of a fish egg in which the eye of the unborn fish is visible from the outside.

fallowing: the process of leaving a salmon farm site empty for a period of time.

farmgate value: the price paid to the salmon farmer for fish. It is counterpart of to the landed value in the commercial fishery.

feed conversion ratio: a ratio that shows the amount of feed required to produce a specified weight gain (e.g., 1 kilogram/2.2 lbs) in farm animals.

Feeds Act: a federal law that specifies which drugs can be used in fish feeds and how medicated feeds must be mixed.

Finfish Aquaculture Waste Control Regulation: a regulation imposed in 2002, under the *Environmental Management Act*, authorizing all finfish farms to "discharge waste, without permits, while ensuring that aquaculture wastes are managed in an environmentally sustainable manner."

***Fisheries Act* (federal)**: a law that requires the proper management and control of fisheries, the conservation and protection of fish, and the protection of fish habitat and prevention of pollution.

Fisheries and Oceans Canada (DFO): the principal federal government ministry responsible for commercial fishing and aquaculture.

Fish Health Database: a collection of data on disease occurrence, sea lice, mortality and other fish-health circumstances at salmon farms. The industry gives the information to the B.C. Salmon Farmers Association, which compiles the data and forwards it to the Ministry of Agriculture and Lands. MAL then posts the figures on its Fish Health website.

Fish Health Management Plan (FHMP): a detailed program of actions taken by salmon farmers to prevent, control and/or treat fish disease. An FHMP must abide by existing provincial regulations and be approved by provincial government authorities.

Formalin: a fungicidal agent used in fish hatcheries.

fry: the life stage of a salmon once the alevin has absorbed its egg sac. Salmon fry are free-swimming.

furunculosis: a disease caused by the *Aeromonas salmonicida* bacteria. It occurs in the Pacific and Atlantic oceans and results in severe hemorrhaging of the internal organs of fish. Although common in fresh water, furunculosis is rare in salt water.

genetically modified salmon: salmon that are produced by the introduction of genetic material from one species to another. Transgenic technology is used to produce certain modifications in plants and animals that could not be made through traditional selection and breeding techniques.

Gillespie Inquiry: a public inquiry into salmon farming, commissioned by the provincial government in 1986 following its moratorium on the expansion of fish farming in B.C.

harmful algal bloom (HAB): a plankton bloom consisting of phytoplankton that produce toxins harmful to other aquatic and/or human life.

harmful alteration, disruption or destruction of fish habitat (HADD): an environmental impact that Fisheries and Oceans Canada (DFO) is mandated to prevent.

Health Canada: the principal federal government ministry that sets standards for food health and safety.

Health Protection Branch: the branch of Health Canada responsible for ensuring that drugs registered and regulated in Canada are safe and effective.

Heath stack: an incubation tray commonly used in hatcheries.

humoral immunity: the ability of a body to fight a pathogen as a result of previous exposure. When the body is first exposed to the pathogen, it produces a protein that targets that pathogen. When it is exposed again, the protein goes into action. Also known as *antibody immunity*.

infectious hematopoeitic necrosis (IHN): the virus that has the greatest impact on farmed Atlantic salmon in B.C. Also known as sockeye disease or sockeye flu, IHN occurs naturally in B.C.'s wild salmon. It attacks the immune system.

infectious salmon anemia (ISA): a naturally occurring virus that has caused significant losses to salmon farmers in Norway, Chile, Scotland and eastern North America. ISA has not been found in B.C., but concerns have been raised about its impacts on farmed and wild salmon stocks should it be introduced to our waters.

International Council for the Exploration of the Sea (ICES): an international organization founded in 1902 to coordinate and promote marine research in the north Atlantic Ocean. ICES works with 1,600 marine scientists from 19 countries around the north Atlantic. Its mandate is to provide unbiased, non-political advice.

Kudoa (*Kudoa thyrsites*): an internal parasite that infects many fishes around the world. It is a normal part of the aquatic environment and, like other parasites, seldom causes mortality in its host. However, it does soften the flesh after harvest, which has caused significant losses to salmon farmers in B.C.

Lepeophtheirus salmonis **(Leps)**: The most predominant sea lice specific to salmonids, but known also to infect non-salmonids. These lice are dark brown in colour and up to 18 mm (0.7 in) long.

listonella: *see* vibriosis.

Ministry of Agriculture and Lands (MAL): the principal provincial government ministry responsible for finfish aquaculture, formerly the Ministry of Agriculture, Food and Fisheries (MAFF).

morts: dead farmed salmon.

natural immunity: the ability of an organism to resist specific pathogens from birth.

night lights: Underwater lights used at some salmon farms to increase the amount of daylight artifically so that the fish will eat more and put on more weight faster than they would in natural daylight.

offal: parts of a fish such as the head, bones and internal organs that are discarded (or recycled) when the fish are processed.

Ovadine: An iodine-based disinfectant used at salmon hatcheries to remove surface bacteria and/or viruses.

pathogen: an agent of disease: a bacteria, virus or parasite that can cause disease.

pigments: *see* carotenoids.

pit-lamping: an illegal fish-harvesting technique in which lights are used at night to attract prey. Pit-lamping was used in the B.C. herring fishery until it was banned more than 30 years ago.

plankton: microscopic animals (zooplankton) and plants (phytoplankton) that drift in the water column.

plankton bloom (*also* **algal bloom)**: the rapid growth of marine algae caused by a particular combination of nutrients, sunlight, salinity and water-column stability. Such blooms can discolour large areas of the ocean. Harmful algal blooms are toxic to aquatic and/or human life.

predator net: a heavy net designed to prevent predators such as seals from attacking salmon in netpens. The net is strung tightly several feet outside the pen holding the fish.

Romet (sulfadimethoxine/ormetoprim): One of the four antibiotics licensed for use at B.C. salmon farms.

salmon (Atlantic): a species of salmon (*Salmo salar*) that belongs to the trout family and represents most of the farmed salmon produced in B.C. These salmon were once native to the Pacific and Atlantic oceans, but are long extinct in the Pacific. Atlantic salmon were never as abundant in the Atlantic as Pacific salmon were (and are) in the Pacific.

salmon (Pacific): the five species are pink (*Oncorhynchus gorbuscha*), chum (*O. keta*), coho (*O. kisutch*), chinook (*O. tshawytscha*) and sockeye (*O. nerka*). Cutthroat trout (*O. clarki*) and steelhead/rainbow trout (*O. mykiss*) are also salmonids.

Salmon Aquaculture Review: A public review of the salmon-farming industry commissioned by the provincial government after it imposed its second moratorium on the granting of new aquaculture licences in 1995. The commission's findings were published as the *Salmon Aquaculture Review* in 1997. Their study was the most comprehensive review of salmon farming ever commissioned in B.C.

separating year classes: a fish management policy in which smolts are not placed in salmon farms containing adult salmon. The practice is designed to prevent any pathogens or lice carried by older fish to be transferred to the smolts, which have not been exposed to any of the harmful bacteria or viruses that may be present and are therefore more susceptible to sickness and infection.

shark net: a heavy net that is stretched below a salmon-farm netpen and typically suspended from predator nets. It is designed to stop predators such as dogfish from attacking the farmed salmon from below.

SLICE: trade name for a parasite treatment containing emamectin benzoate. It is reported by veterinarians to kill all stages of sea lice within two to four weeks and said to be effective at preventing reinfection for up to 14 weeks. In 2005 it was awaiting approval by Health Canada, and could only be used under Health Canada's Emergency Drug Release program.

smolting: the process by which salmon develop to the point where they can survive in salt water. The mottled parr marks that help camouflage fry in the gravel of a stream are replaced by a silver burnish, and scales begin to form to protect the fish in the ocean environment. Kidney and gill functions also change in order to deal with salt ions in sea water.

smolts: young salmon that have developed to the point where they can survive in salt water.

tenure: a licence or lease issued by the Crown to occupy publicly owned foreshore. There are 128 saltwater salmon-farming tenures in B.C. and seven freshwater tenures on lakes.

Terramycin Aqua (oxytetracycline): a broad-spectrum antibiotic, one of the four antibiotics licensed for use at B.C. salmon farms.

Transplant Committee: a federal committee that oversees the import of salmon eggs to Canada. The movement of eggs around B.C. is jointly administered by the federal and provincial governments.

Transport Canada: a federal government ministry whose Environmental Assessment Division conducts screenings under the *Canadian Environmental Assessment Act*. Transport Canada's Navigable Waters Protection Division reviews applications for salmon-farm tenures for navigational concerns.

Tribrissen (sulfadiazine/ trimethoprim): one of the four antibiotics licensed for use at B.C. salmon farms.

United Nations Food and Agriculture Organization (FAO): an organization founded in 1945 that "leads international efforts to defeat hunger." FAO helps developing nations modernize and improve agriculture, forestry and fisheries practices. It provides a neutral forum where all nations meet as equals to negotiate agreements and debate policy. FAO is also a source of knowledge and information about world capture fisheries and aquaculture.

vaccination: a disease-prevention practice in which the body is exposed to a small amount of a pathogen— typically dead, inactive or altered so it is non-pathogenic. The body responds by developing antibodies specific to that pathogen, and when exposed again, the antibodies can either destroy the pathogen, limit its ability to gain a foothold or reduce its effects. Most farmed salmon produced in B.C. are vaccinated against the common pathogens in the environment before they are transferred from their freshwater hatcheries into saltwater netpens.

Veterinary Drugs Directorate (VDD): part of the Health Products and Food Branch of Health Canada, mandated to "protect human and animal health and the safety of Canada's food supply." VDD evaluates and monitors

the safety, quality and effectiveness, sets standards, and promotes
the prudent use of veterinary drugs
administered to food-producing and
companion animals." VDD also releases
drugs such as SLICE under Health
Canada's Emergency Drug Release
program.

vibriosis (listonella): a disease whose
symptoms include internal hemorrhaging, systemic (methodical) infections and sometimes deep red ulcers
on the skin. The disease is caused by
naturally occurring *Vibrio* species,
which affect wild saltwater fish and

invertebrates around the world. *Vibrio
anguillarum* and *Vibrio ordalli* are of
most concern to salmon farmers. They
affect farmed Pacific and Atlantic
salmon.

Waste Management Act: a provincial
law that regulates the discharge of
organic and non-organic waste. The
Finfish Aquaculture Waste Regulation
and the Land Based Finfish Aquaculture Regulation, which fall under the
Waste Management Act, are designed in
part to ensure that production of waste
at a salmon farm does not exceed the
site's ability to assimilate it.

Salmon Aquaculture Websites

SALMON-FARMING COMPANIES
Creative Salmon
www.creativesalmon.com

Mainstream Canada
www.cermaq.com/
Main corporate website of Cermaq
in Norway

Marine Harvest
www.marineharvest.com
Head office website of the world's
largest farmed-salmon producer,
based in Norway.

Target Marine Group
www.targetmarine.com
Largest B.C.-owned salmon-farming
company. Operates on the Sunshine
Coast.

Yellow Island Aquaculture
www.yellowislandaquaculture.com/
Small family-owned salmon-farming
company on Quadra Island.

GROUPS THAT SUPPORT SALMON FARMING
**British Columbia Salmon Farmers
Association**
www.salmonfarmers.org
B.C.'s largest industry organization.
It is the group most often quoted in the
media, and it posts information on
major issues.

**Canadian Aquaculture Industry
Alliance**
www.aquaculture.ca
Canada's largest pro-aquaculture organization. The site focuses on farmed-salmon
food safety and environmental issues.

Northern Aquaculture
www.naqua.com
Site of *Northern Aquaculture* magazine,
the largest aquaculture publication in
Canada, "the voice of cold water aquaculture in North America."

Salmon of the Americas
www.salmonoftheamericas.com
An extensive U.S.-based website, but relevant to B.C. Its mission statement is: "Salmon of the Americas is an organization of salmon-producing companies in Canada, Chile and the United States whose mission is to improve health, awareness and dining enjoyment of consumers in North America by providing timely, complete, accurate and insightful information about salmon on behalf of the member companies."

Society for the Positive Awareness of Aquaculture
www.farmfreshsalmon.org
A grassroots B.C. organization whose mission statement is: "To promote positive awareness of the aquaculture industry through public education, and community involvement."

GROUPS THAT OPPOSE SALMON FARMING

Farmed and Dangerous
www.farmedanddangerous.org/
Site for the Coastal Alliance for Aquaculture Reform. Their Farmed and Dangerous campaign was mounted to persuade consumers to stop eating farmed salmon.

Georgia Strait Alliance
www.georgiastrait.org
Addresses salmon farming and other issues that affect the Strait of Georgia, and produces a report card on the state of the B.C. salmon aquaculture industry.

Raincoast Research Society
www.raincoastresearch.org/
    salmon-farming.htm
Researches and publishes information on the impacts of Atlantic salmon farming in B.C.

Sierra Legal Defence Fund
www.sierralegal.org
Organization that seeks environmental protection through litigation, provides free legal services to environmental groups and concerned citizens, and posts news and information on salmon farming and other issues.

David Suzuki Foundation
www.davidsuzuki.org
Largest environmental non-governmental agency in B.C. Salmon farming is a major portion of its work, but a variety of other issues are addressed.

Watershed Watch
www.watershed-watch.org
A member of the B.C. Coastal Alliance for Aquaculture Reform (CAAR). The mission statement is: "To protect wild salmon, coastal ecosystems and human health from destructive fish farming practices."

PROVINCIAL GOVERNMENT

Ministry of Agriculture and Lands— General
www.agf.gov.bc.ca/fisheries
General site for the ministry, with lots of information on B.C. salmon aquaculture.

Ministry of Agriculture and Lands— Fish Health
www.agf.gov.bc.ca/fisheries/health/
    index.htm
Maintains the Fish Health Database, reports on disease and sea lice at salmon farms, deals with fish-health management, provides information on disease and drug use.

Ministry of Agriculture and Lands— Licensing and Compliance

www.agf.gov.bc.ca/fisheries/compl/ ce_main.htm

Issues commercial aquaculture and seafood licences, monitors and inspects the aquaculture industry, ensures that regulations are being followed and environmental standards are adhered to. Compliance reports are posted.

Ministry of Environment

www.env.gov.bc.ca/epd/epdpa/industrial _waste/agriculture/aqua_home.htm

Regulates and monitors salmon-farm waste. Administers the Finfish Aquaculture Waste Control Regulation.

Integrated Land Management Bureau (formerly Land and Water British Columbia)

www.lwbc.bc.ca

Late in 2005, this bureau, a Crown corporation that had managed the allocation of Crown land and water resources on behalf of the B.C. government, was being divided among several different ministries, including the Integrated Land Management Bureau of the Ministry of Agriculture and Lands.

Environmental Assessment Office

www.eao.gov.bc.ca/

The Environmental Assessment Office (EAO) is a neutral provincial agency that coordinates assessment of the impacts of major development proposals in British Columbia.

FEDERAL GOVERNMENT

Fisheries and Oceans Canada (DFO)— General

www.dfo-mpo.gc.ca/index.htm

Principal federal government ministry responsible for aquaculture.

Fisheries and Oceans Canada— Pacific Region

www.pac.dfo-mpo.gc.ca/aquaculture

DFO's Pacific Region aquaculture website.

Fisheries and Oceans Canada— Atlantic Salmon Watch Program (ASWP)

www.pac.dfo-mpo.gc.ca/sci/aqua/ aswp_e.htm

Monitors escapes from salmon farms and conducts research into the impacts of escaped Atlantic salmon on wild salmon stocks in B.C.

Health Canada—Canadian Food Inspection Agency (CFIA)

www.inspection.gc.ca

Site includes acts, regulations, product information, inspection manuals and procedures, details of the quality management program and other reference materials.

Health Canada—Veterinary Drugs Directorate

www.hc-sc.gc.ca/vetdrugs-medsvet/

A website operated by Health Canada's Bureau of Veterinary Drugs that provides maximum allowable residues of antibiotics and drugs and other information. Data regarding the B.C. salmon-farming industry and the drugs associated with it can be requested from this site.

Agriculture and Agri-Food Canada

www.agr.gc.ca/

Co-manages the fish and seafood industry with Fisheries and Oceans Canada.

Selected Bibliography

In addition to the books, magazines and reports listed below, many issues of *Northern Aquaculture* magazine, *IntraFish* magazine, daily web postings, FishNET listserve, government websites, government annual reports, local newspapers and salmon-farming websites were consulted. Dozens of people in industry, government and academia were interviewed. Nearly 100 letters to the editor, web postings, personal communications, papers and articles by Alexandra Morton also served as source material.

Alaska Department of Fish and Game. "Atlantic Salmon: A White Paper," March 5, 2002.

Anderson, Terry. "Alien Invasion." *B.C. Outdoors Sport Fishing*, May 2002.

Asgard, Torbjorn, et al. "Top Resource Exploitation in Norwegian Salmon Farming." Nutreco, 1995.

Barlow, S.M. "The World Market Overview of Fish Meal and Fish Oil." Paper presented to 2nd Seafood By-Products Conference, Alaska, November 2002.

Barrett, Dick. "Alaska Fish Contaminants." Alaska Departttment of Environmental Conservation, Division of Environmental Health, 2001.

Beamish, R.J., et al. "Sea Lice on Adult Pacific Salmon in the Coastal Waters of Central British Columbia, Canada." *Fisheries Research*, Vol. 76, 2005.

British Columbia. Auditor General. "Salmon Forever: An Assessment of the Provincial Role in Sustaining Wild Salmon," October 2004.

British Columbia. Ministry of Agriculture, Food and Fisheries. "Comparison of PFRCC Report on Aquaculture (2003) to Salmon Aquaculture Review (1997)." 2003.

————. "Finfish Aquaculture Waste Control Regulations." September 2002.

———. "Guide to Information Requirements for Marine Finfish Aquaculture Applications." May 2003.

———. "Sea Lice Monitoring Program 2004/2005." 2004.

———. "2nd Annual Inspection Report on Marine Finfish Aquaculture Sites." February 2002.

———. "Status of Implementation of Salmon Aquaculture Review Recommendations." April 2003.

———. "Status of Salmon Aquaculture Review Recommendations." January 2002.

———. "The 2002 British Columbia Seafood Industry Year in Review." 2002.

——— and Land and Water British Columbia. "Marine Finfish Aquaculture Plan Form." May 2003.

——— and Ministry of Water, Land and Air Protection. "3rd Annual Inspection Report on Marine Finfish Aquaculture Sites." August 2003.

British Columbia. Ministry of Environment Lands and Parks. "Environmental Assessment Office Report of the Salmon Aquaculture Review." 1997.

———. "Marine Salmon Farming Compliance Report." April 2001.

———. "Salmon Aquaculture Waste Management and Update review" (G3 Consulting), December 2000.

British Columbia. Ministry of Finance and Corporate Relations. "British Columbia's Fish Products and Seafood Industry in the 1990s." May 2001

———. Ministry of Management Services. "British Columbia's Fisheries and Aquaculture Sector." September 2002.

British Columbia Salmon Farmers Association. *Careers in Aquaculture.* November 10, 1999.

Brooks, Dr. Kenneth M. "An Assessment of Whether Pink Salmon (*Oncorhynchus gorbuscha*) Runs in the Broughton Archipelago of British Columbia, Canada, Are Threatened by Sea Lice (*Lepeophtheirus salmonis*) Infections Originating on Cultured Atlantic Salmon (*Salmon salar*)." Port Townsend WA: Aquatic Environmental Sciences, June 2003.

———. "The Effects of Water Temperature, Salinity, and Currents on the Survival and Distribution of the Infective Copepodid Stage of Sea Lice (Lepeophtheirus Salmonis) Originating on Atlantic Salmon Farms in the Broughton Archipelago of British Columbia, Canada)." Port Townsend WA: Aquatic Environmental Sciences, 2004.

Campbell, Leslie. "For Love of Home."*Focus on Women*, January 2004.

Canada. Auditor General. "The Effects of Salmon Farming in British Columbia on the Management of Wild Salmon Stocks," 2000.

Canada. Canadian Food Inspection Agency. "Contaminant Results in Fish Feed, Fish Meal and Fish Oil" Report, May 2002.

Canada. Fisheries and Oceans Canada. "Achieving the Vision: Report of the Commissioner for Aquaculture Development." 2003.

———. "DFO's Aquaculture's Policy Framework." 2002.

———. "Recommendations for Change" (Report of the Commissioner for Aquaculture Development). 2004.

———. "Studies of Early Marine Survival of Pacific Salmon and Sea Lice Occurrence in Queen Charlotte Strait." December 2001.

Canada. Health Canada. "Food Safety Assessment Program." June 2001.

———. "Nutrient Value of Some Common Foods." 1999.

——— and Pest Management Regulatory Agency. "Integrated Pest Management of Sea Lice in Salmon Aquaculture." March 2003.

Canada. Senate Committee on Fisheries. "Aquaculture in Canada's Atlantic and Pacific Regions." Interim report of the committee, June 2001.

Canada. Standing Committee on Fisheries and Oceans. "The Federal Role in Aquaculture in Canada." April 2003.

Canadian Alliance for Aquaculture Reform. "Why You Should Think Twice About Eating Salmon." Information bulletin, no date.

Chary, Lin Kaatz. "Persistent Organic Pollutants in Alaska: What Does Science Tell Us?" Circumpolar Conservation Union, October 2000.

Coastal Alliance for Aquaculture Reform. "Farmed and Dangerous." Brochure, no date.

Commissioner for Aquaculture Development. "Achieving the Vision." Fisheries and Oceans Canada, 2003.

——— and R.G. Peterson. "Potential Genetic Interaction Between Wild and Farm Salmon of the Same Species." Fisheries and Oceans Canada, September 1999.

Dean, Ashley. "High Risk to Northwest Fisheries" (summary of Stanford University Fisheries Policy Project report). *Fisherman Life*, November 2003.

Demont, John. "The Empty Seas." *Maclean's*, November 3, 2003.

Economist. "The Promise of a Blue Revolution." Special Report. August 9, 2003.

Edwards, Rob. "Farm Salmon Is Now Most Contaminated Food on Shelf." *Sunday Herald*, October 20, 2002.

———. "Fish Farming Pollution Is Up By 100%. Opponents Cite 'Damning' Figures But Industry Dismisses Impact as 'Minute'." *Sunday Herald*, May 18, 2003.

Environmental Working Group. "PCB's in Farmed Salmon." 2003.

Evenden A.J., et al. *Renibacterium Salmoninarum and Bacterial Kidney Disease: The Unfinished Jigsaw.* New York: Pergamon Press, 1993.

Ellis, David W. and Associates. "Net Loss: The Salmon Netcage Industry in British Columbia." Vancouver: David Suzuki Foundation, 1996.

Fishmeal Information Network. "Fishmeal Facts and Figures." 2004.

Fleming, Ian A., Bror Jonsson and Mart R. Gross. "Phenotypic Divergence of Sea-ranched, Farmed and Wild Salmon." *Canadian Journal of Fisheries and Aquatics Sciences*, 1992.

Forster, John. "An Aquaculture Chicken, Salmon—A Case Study" (pre-publication draft, published with the support of the International Salmon Farmers Association). No date (published after 1997).

Friends of the Earth. "Fish Farm Dangers, Escape Facts and Figures of Farmed Salmon" (website fact sheet). 2000.

Gallaugher, Patricia, et al., eds. "Speaking for the Salmon: Proceedings of the Summit of Scientists on Sea Lice." Simon Fraser University, Burnaby, July 2, 2002.

Gifford, K. Dun. Lecture on sustainable aquaculture. Canadian Aquaculture Conference, Victoria, October 2003.

Groot, C., L. Margolis and W. C. Clarke, eds. *Physiological Ecology of Pacific Salmon*. Vancouver: UBC Press and Government of Canada, Fisheries and Oceans Canada, 1995.

Hatfield Consultants and EVS Environmental Consultants. "Environmental Effects of Salmon Netcage Culture in British Columbia: A Literature Review." Victoria: Ministry of Environment, Lands and Parks, April 1996.

Hawaleshka, Danylo. "Tainted Food." *Maclean's*, January 2004.

Hites, Ronald, et al. "Global Assessment of Organic Contaminants in Farmed Salmon." *Science*, Vol. 303, January 2004.

———. "Global Assessment of Polybrominated Diphenyl Ethers in Farmed and Wild Salmon." *Environmental Science and Technology*, August 10, 2005.

Hume, Stephen, et al. *A Stain Upon the Sea: West Coast Salmon Farming*. Maderia Park B.C.: Harbour Publishing, 2004.

IntraFish, "Fishmeal and Oil or Vegetable Alternatives" (industry report). March 3, 2001.

Keller, Betty C., and Rosella Leslie. *Sea-Silver: Inside British Columbia's Salmon-Farming Industry*. Victoria: Horsdal and Schubart, 1996.

Kenney, E. Allan, "Net Gain: The Salmon Farming Industry in B.C." B.C. Salmon Farmers Association, January 1997.

Knapp, Gunnar, "Change, Challenges and Opportunities for Wild Fisheries." Talk given at Conference on Marine Aquaculture. Victoria, November 18, 2003.

———. "Implications of Aquaculture for Wild Fisheries: The Case of Alaska Wild Salmon." Talk given at Bevan Sustainable Fisheries Seminar. University of Washington, Seattle, February 10, 2005.

Krieberg, Henrik, and W.J. Craig Clarke. "Returns of Chinook Salmon Released from the Experimental Mariculture Facility in Departure Bay" (abstract), Fisheries and Oceans Canada, May 2003.

Krkosek, Martin, Mark A. Lewis and John P. Volpe. "Transmission Dynamics of Parasitic Sea Lice from Farm to Wild Salmon." Proceedings of the Royal Society B, March 30, 2005.

Krummel, E.M., et al., "Delivery of Pollutants by Spawning Salmon." Nature, Vol. 425, September 18, 2003.

Langer, Otto E. "Is there a Bottom Line in the Wild Salmon–Farmed Salmon Debate?: A Technical Opinion." Vancouver: David Suzuki Foundation, March 2003.

Lanteigne, Stephen. "Current Status and Potential of the Canadian Aquaculture Industry." Office of the Commissioner for Aquaculture Development, December 2002.

Leggatt, Stuart. "Clear Choices, Clean Waters: Report and Recommendations of the Leggatt Inquiry into Salmon Farming in British Columbia." Vancouver: David Suzuki Foundation, November 2001.

Magdoff, Fred, John Bellamy Foster and Frederick H. Buttell, eds. Hungry for Profit. New York: Monthly Review Press, 2000.

Manning Richard. Food's Frontier: The Next Green Revolution. London: University of California Press, 2000.

Marshall, Dave. "Fishy Business: The Economics of Salmon Farming in B.C." Report for Canadian Centre for Policy Alternatives, Vancouver, July 2003.

McRae, Donald M., and Peter H. Pearse, "Treaties and Transitions." Victoria: Minister of Fisheries and Oceans, Minister Responsible for Treaty Negotiations, Ministry of Agriculture, Food and Fisheries, July 2003.

Meggs, Geoff. Salmon: The Decline of the British Columbia Fishery. Vancouver: Douglas & McIntyre, 1991.

Montaigne, Fen. "Everybody Loves Atlantic Salmon: Here's the Catch." National Geographic, July 2003.

Myers, Ransom A., and Boris Worm. "Rapid Worldwide Depletion of Predatory Fish Communities." Letters, Nature, May 15, 2003.

Nash, Colin, ed. "The Net-pen Salmon Farming Industry in the Pacific Northwest." U.S. Department of Commerce/NOAA Technical Memorandum NMFS-NWFSC-49, September 2001.

Noakes, Scott R.J., et al. "Chinook Salmon Impede Atlantic Salmon Conservation in Lake Ontario." Ecology of Freshwater Fish, 2003.

Nudds, Kristy. "Fish, Omega-3 Fatty Acids and You." University of Guelph, October 2002.

Nutreco, "Social and Environmental Report." 2002.

O'Neill, Sandra M., James E. West and James C. Hoeman. "Spatial Trends in the Concentration of Polychlorinated Biphenyls in Chinook and Coho salmon in Puget Sound and Factors Affecting PCB Accumulation: Results from the Puget Sound Ambient Monitoring Program." Olympia WA: Washington Department of Fish and Wildlife, 1998.

Pacific Fisheries Resource Council. "Advisory: Wild Salmon and Aquaculture in British Columbia."January 2003.

———. "Making Sense of the Debate about Hatchery Impacts, Interactions Between Enhanced and Wild Salmon on Canada's Pacific Coast." March 2004.

———. "Making Sense of the Salmon Aquaculture Debate." January 2003.

Parfitt, Ben. "To Raise a Fish." *Shared Vision*, November 2003.

Pew Oceans Commission. "America's Living Oceans: Charting a Course for Sea Change." May 2003.

Porter, Gareth. "Protecting Wild Atlantic Salmon from Impacts of Salmon Aquaculture: Country-by-Country Progress Report." World Wildlife Fund and Atlantic Salmon Federation, May 2003.

Price Waterhouse Coopers. "Salmon Farming Overview: 2000." Presentation to Salmon Farmers Association annual general meeting, July 2001.

——— and British Columbia, Ministry of Agriculture, Food and Fisheries. "A Competitiveness Survey of the British Columbia Salmon Farming Industry," May 2003.

Richard, John. "Sea Lice in North America: Experiences and Concerns." British Columbia Aquaculture Research and Development Council, May 1991.

Robbins, John. *Diet for a New America*, Tiburon: Stillpoint Publishing, 1987.

Roheim, Cathy A. "Early Indications of Market Impacts from the Marine Stewardship Council's Ecolabeling of Seafood." Report for U.S. Department of Environmental and Natural Resource Economics, University of Rhode Island, December 2002.

Rolston, David, and Bart Proctor. "A Baseline Report of the Incidence of Sea Lice on Juvenile Salmonids on British Columbia's North Coast, Salmon Farms and Sea Lice." Vancouver: David Suzuki Foundation, 2002.

Sadar, M. Husain. "Catalysing More Debate on Environmental Impact Assessment." Guest editorial, Impact Assessment and Project Appraisal, December 2002.

SeaFood Business. "Farmed Salmon: Fact or Fiction." June 2003.

Schering-Plough Animal Health Corporation. "Potential Environmental Impacts of Emamectin Benzoate, formulated SLICE, for Salmonids." New Jersey: Animal Pharm Consulting Group, July 2004.

Scottish Association for Marine Science. "Ecological Effects of Sea Lice Medicines in Scottish Sea Lochs." February 2005.

Shepherd, C.J., I.H. Pike and S.M. Barlow. "Sustainable Feed Resources of Marine Origin." European Aquaculture Society Special Publication Number 35, June 2005.

Sierra Legal Defence Fund. "Coalition Challenges Feds to Stop Spread of Disease in B.C.'s Fish." Media release, June 9, 2005.

Staniford, Don. "Sea Cage Fish Farming: An Evaluation of Environmental and Public Health Aspects (the Five Fundamental Flaws of Sea Cage Fish Farming): Excerpts of Presentation to European Parliament's Public Hearing on Aquaculture in the European Union..." October 1, 2002.

Suzuki (David) Foundation. "Diseases Associated with Salmon Farms." Information bulletin, no date.

———. "Drugs Used in Salmon Farming Industry." Information bulletin, no date.

———. "Escaping Farmed Salmon Pose Risks to Wild Species." Information bulletin, no date.

———. "Net Loss of Wild Fish to Produce Farmed Salmon." Information bulletin, no date.

———. "Open Netcage Fish Farm Pollution." Information bulletin, no date.

———. "Salmon Farm Pollution." Information bulletin, no date.

———. "Solutions for Salmon Farming." Information bulletin, no date.

———. "Sustainable Fishing." Information bulletin, no date.

Sweeting, R.M., et al. "Replacement of Wild Coho Salmon by Hatchery-Reared Coho Salmon in the Strait of Georgia Over the Past Three Decades." *North American Journal of Fisheries Management*, Vol. 23, 2003.

Tidwell, James H., and Geoff L. Allan. "Fish as Food: Aquaculture's Contribution." EMBO Reports, Vol. 2, No. III, European molecular Biology Organization, 2001.

United Nations. Food and Agriculture Organization. "The State of World Fisheries and Aquaculture." 2002.

United States. Department of Agriculture. "Nutrient Database for Standard Reference, Release 16-1 (2004)." web database, USDA, 2004.

van Dongen, John. "Why B.C. Lifted the Moratorium on Fish Farms." Opinion editorial, Ministry of Agriculture, Food and Fisheries, 2002.

Vannuccini, Stefania. "Overview of Fish Production, Utilization, Consumption and Trade, 2001 Data." UN Food Food and Agriculture Organization, 2003.

Volpe, John. "Super un-Natural: Atlantic Salmon in B.C. Waters." Public report for David Suzuki Foundation, 2001.

Waknitz, William F. "Comparing the Impacts of Commercial Salmon Fishing with Commercial Salmon Farming." *Northern Aquaculture*, December 2003.

———, Robert N. Iwamoto and Mark S. Strom. "Interactions of Atlantic Salmon in the Pacific Northwest: Impacts on Eco-systems." *Fisheries Research*, Vol. 62, 2003.

Watershed Watch. "Salmon Farms, Sea Lice and Wild Salmon." December 2001.

Webber, Michael. "What Price Farmed Fish: A Review of the Environmental and Social Costs of Farming Carnivorous Fish." Executive summary prepared for SeaWeb, July 2003.

Weiss, Kenneth R. "Fish Farms Become Feedlots of the Sea." *Los Angeles Times*, December 9, 2002.

Index